BASIC business anal
and operations resea

G000166569

Butterworths BASIC Series includes the following titles:

BASIC aerodynamics
BASIC artificial intelligence
BASIC business analysis and operations research
BASIC economics
BASIC hydraulics
BASIC hydrodynamics
BASIC hydrology
BASIC interactive graphics
BASIC investment appraisal
BASIC materials studies
BASIC matrix methods
BASIC mechanical vibrations
BASIC molecular spectroscopy
BASIC numerical mathematics
BASIC operational amplifiers
BASIC soil mechanics
BASIC statistics
BASIC stress analysis
BASIC theory of structures
BASIC thermodynamics and heat transfer

BASIC business analysis and operations research

R H Mole BSc, MSc, PhD, AFIMA
Lecturer, Department of Management Studies,
Loughborough University of Technology, Loughborough, England

Butterworths
London . Boston . Durban . Singapore . Sydney . Toronto . Wellington

First published 1987

© Butterworth & Co. (Publishers) Ltd, 1987

British Library Cataloguing in Publication Data

Mole, R.H.
    BASIC business analysis and operations research. —
    (Butterworths BASIC series)
    1. Operations research — Data processing
    2. BASIC (Computer program language)
    I. Title
    658.4′034′02855133   HD30.25
    ISBN 0–408–01590–X

Library of Congress Cataloging-in-Publication Data

Mole, R.H. (Richard H.)
    BASIC business analysis and operations research.

    (Butterworths BASIC series)
    Includes index.
    1. Industrial management—Mathematical models.
2. Operations research—Data processing.   3. BASIC
(Computer program language)   I. Title.   II. Series.
HD30.25.M66   1987   658.4′034′0285526   86-26398
ISBN 0–408–01590–X

Phototypeset by Scribe Design, Gillingham, Kent
Printed and bound in England by Page Bros (Norwich) Ltd, Norfolk

Preface

Mathematical models can be used to analyse business problems in order to heighten managements' understanding of the issues. This approach can result in better decisions and more robust long-term strategy. The process has become known as Operations Research (OR) and micros are commonly used for the numerical aspects of the work.

The purpose of this book is to introduce the reader to the application of the computer language called BASIC to a selection of material from the core curriculum of OR mathematical models. It fills the gap which has been left between the texts on the 'Management application of computers' and the texts on 'Operations research techniques'. It is both a reader, showing how the micro can solve computational problems effectively and efficiently, and a workbook which provides a graded series of programming tasks. The reader should therefore have easy access to a computer. A primary aim is to build competence and confidence in a reader's ability to design well-structured programs for computational problems in a management context. At the same time the underlying theory has been presented as fully as space allows. The writer has kept constantly in mind the needs of the independent learner, and on average each chapter ends with a dozen programming exercises.

This book is intended primarily for introductory use by undergraduate management, computer, technology and science students. The elementary sections are suitable for business studies and school students who wish to see just how useful modern approaches can be to the analysis of business operations. But science and technology graduates will also find it a useful introduction to 'OR on the micro'.

The qualities of the computer language BBC BASIC have something in common with the qualities of the spoken English language which characterize BBC broadcasts. The listener to BBC English will appreciate the clear enunciation and clear grammatical construction. It is easy to follow. The reader will also find it easy to take in the sense of a BBC BASIC program. But there is no more compulsion to employ the BBC BASIC dialect in one's programming tasks than there is to adopt BBC English for all everyday communication. The choice of BBC BASIC for this book is in the reader's interests, whatever the dialect of BASIC supported by his or her computer.

The choice of material from the OR core curriculum is made in the context of the Butterworths' BASIC series as a whole, because it is desirable to avoid unnecessary overlap with the material of companion volumes. The choice is also constrained by the available space. Companion volumes cover contiguous material:

BASIC business simulation by P J Stratfold, (forthcoming)
BASIC forecasting by D G Johnson and M King, (forthcoming)
BASIC investment appraisal by R H Mole, Butterworths, 1985
BASIC matrix methods by J C Mason, Butterworths, 1984
BASIC numerical mathematics by J C Mason, Butterworths, 1983
BASIC statistics by J Tennant-Smith, Butterworths. 1985

Chapters 1 and 2 are brief introductions to the BASIC language and to the field of Business Operations Research. Chapter 3 deals with Index Numbers, which are conceptually fairly straightforward and of immediate importance to any businessman. It provides a gentle introduction to programming in structured BASIC. A number of programs for Data Fitting are developed in Chapter 4. These are described in the context of cost-volume relationships, an essential tool for financial analysis and control.

Critical Path Network Analysis is the topic of Chapter 5, which illustrates how a simple program can be developed to include progressive complexity. The fully developed program utilizes the graphics facilities of modern micros to display a critical path planning network. In Chapter 6 on Linear Programming, several programs are given for a range of computational tasks, from a complete enumeration of the vertices of the feasible region to an implementation of the two-phase simplex method for mixed linear inequalities. A final chapter considers Markov chains in the context of policies for preventative maintenance.

The writer would like to record his gratitude to all those who contributed to this book, and especially to Don Goodsell of Butterworths who guided the project to completion, to Rodger Mustoe who did his best to find the bugs in the programs, to R H Mole Senior for dropping everything to read the manuscript for grammatical errors and lack of clarity, to Geof Gregory and John Wilson for their comments on Chapter 6, to colleagues, especially

David Johnson, for being there in the background and ready to listen and help when needed, to Felicity Nash for secretarial assistance, to Joyce Savage for keeping the computing equipment in excellent order, and to my family for putting up with it all!

I acknowledge the permission of the Chartered Association of Certified Accountants to reproduce a few past examination questions.

R H Mole

Contents

Chapter 1

Introduction to BASIC

1.1 Dialects of the BASIC language

BASIC is a powerful and flexible computer language. It is easy to learn and it is supported on all modern micros. BASIC is also easy to apply to most mathematical models of operations research. The use of the microcomputer removes the tedium from repetitive calculations, so allowing concentration on the ideas which underpin the calculations. The inevitable price for these considerable advantages is that scrupulous attention has to be paid to detail, both in design and in implementation of BASIC computer programs.

BASIC was devised in the 1960s at Dartmouth College, USA, to provide a Beginners All-purpose Symbolic Instruction Code. Over the years it has evolved into many closely related dialects, as computer manufacturers have sought to give their products a competitive edge. This is particularly true of the last few years with the mass availability of small but highly efficient microcomputers. As a result the BASIC dialect of a modern micro is almost always an advance on the dialect available on the large mainframe machine. The best BASICs encourage the user to write 'structured' programs which are relatively easy to read and debug.

Three excellent instructional manuals on BASIC are cited at the end of this chapter for the reader who needs a general introduction. This short chapter assumes that the reader has already some acquaintance or familiarity with BASIC. Its purpose is to emphasize the main points, paying special attention to particular aspects which in my experience students find difficult to appreciate.

The adoption by the British Broadcasting Corporation of the Acorn micro for a series of popular computer education programmes has resulted in the label 'BBC' attaching both to the Acorn micro itself and to the Acorn BASIC dialect. In this book the BBC BASIC dialect has been preferred for several reasons. First, the great majority of British school children who learn computing languages will have been introduced to BBC BASIC through use of the Acorn BBC Model B Micro or the BBC Master series of micros. Second, it is possibly the best implementation of BASIC in its own right, and so is widely used in further and higher education. Third, it is easy to make minor alterations to the programs in this book to allow them to run on any modern microcomputer. This chapter describes how a few extra statements can ensure compatibility with even the most primitive BASIC dialect.

1.2 Assignment and non-executable statements

The instructions which are held within a BASIC program are known as statements, and they may be entered into the machine in any sequence. Each statement is begun by a unique line number and the computer will sort the statements on entry according to numerical order. When a program is RUN the computer will slavishly 'execute' these statements, stopping prematurely only if a syntax error is discovered. Errors may be edited out in three ways: an existing statement is overwritten if a new statement is typed in with the same line number; typing the line number followed immediately by pressing the RETURN key will remove a statement entirely; it is easy to make small amendments within a statement by the use of a COPY key and the 'cursor control' in conjunction with normal keyboard entry.

Most statements 'do' something or other, with the exception of the END statement which signals the end of the program, REM statements which contain REMarks by the programmer that are not executed by the machine, and blank statements which break up segments of statements. This last cosmetic device can contribute greatly to the clarity of a program, but it is only available in some BASICs (by typing a space after the line number before pressing the RETURN key).

An assignment statement is used for carrying out arithmetic operations, as in

```
7010  X = (X + 2*X^3 ) / 4 - 2
```

Statement 7010 looks superficially like an equation, but it is an instruction to replace the current numerical value of the variable X by the expression on the right-hand side. Primitive BASIC dialects will require the insertion of the word LET after the line number. Notice that blank spaces may be introduced at will to aid legibility, and also that there is little value in 'simplifying' the expression by standard algebraic procedures. If the value of X were zero prior to the execution of statement 7010 then the new value after execution would be −2. This is because an assignment statement containing arithmetic operators is evaluated according to a hierarchical system of priorities, working from left to right within the following priorities:

(˰)	parentheses	First	priority
	exponentiation	Second	priority
× and /	multiplication and division	Third	priority
+ and −	addition and subtraction	Fourth	priority

BBC BASIC automatically initializes numeric variables at zero prior to RUNning a program, but primitive dialects may not, and they can therefore produce bizarre output unless the user explicitly initializes all numeric variables prior to use, as in

```
10  X = 0 : Y = 0 : Z = 0
```

The programs in this book will generally, but not invariably, initialize variables in this way. Notice that line 10 is an instance of a multiple statement line, ie the colons indicate the presence of three independent statements. Some multiple statement lines are employed when it helps to achieve clarity of expression. Since statements are normally numbered here in multiples of 10, the reader who is restricted to a BASIC which cannot accept multiple statement lines will always be able to proceed by inserting a series of additional single statements on successive lines.

1.3 Variables, arrays and standard functions

The names of numeric variables in BBC BASIC may be long, subject to certain restrictions which can be found in the appropriate manuals. For instance Variable__X5 could be substituted for X in statement 7010, and long names can on occasion make an important contribution to program clarity. If your BASIC will not support long names then you should improvise short ones, keeping a detailed list in a REM statement as a reminder and to guard against the risk of using the same variable for two parallel purposes. The choice of variable name depends upon some relatively close association in the mind of the programmer, e.g. verbal as in the variable named Interest, or algebraic as in the variable X.

String variables are not restricted to numeric quantities. They are automatically initialized to the 'null' string in BBC BASIC and they may be assigned text composed of alphanumeric quantities. String variables are identified to the computer by the dollar character $ postfixed to the string variable name, and the string value must be enclosed in quotation marks in any assignment, as in

```
7020  month3$ = "March"
```

The statement in line 20 below is a DIM statement which reserves storage for a string array Month$, which could store not only the months of the year in Month$(1) to Month$(12), say, but also further information in the 'first' element, such as Month$(0)="1986 − Industry Year". Primitive BASICs may not support a zero argument for an array, however, and readers may have to improvise an ordinary string variable in substitution. Statement 7030 below assigns 'March' to the element Month$(3) as a consequence of the preceding statement 7020.

A variable array is a natural choice when representing subscripted algebraic variables and matrices. For instance, the coefficient in the Ith row and the Jth column of matrix A could be stored in the element A(I,J) of a two-dimensional array A. Statement 20 also has the effect of reserving memory for a two-dimensional numeric array A. This can cater for the elements of a matrix with 12 rows and 31 columns (or 13 and 32 if one includes zero arguments). It could be used, for example, to record the daily turnover in a DIY retail store which opens every day of the month.

```
20    DIM A(12,31) , Month$(12)
7030  Month$(3) = month3$
```

The computer has a range of built-in standard functions which share a superficial resemblance to arrays, but they have a different purpose and do not involve DIM statements. Thus

SQR(X) finds $X^{.5}$
LOG(X) finds the logarithm of X to base 10
LN(X)   finds the natural logarithm of X
STR$(X)finds the string equivalent of X, i.e. "X"
etc

These are also instances of reserved words which cannot be used as variable names, or even to start off longer variable names, due to the ambiguity which would result. For instance, the variable named LOGISTIC is invalid, though Logistic is valid.

1.4 Input and output

Data can be read using READ and DATA statements, or from a data file. The programs in this book utilize neither method, but the exercises call for the reader to develop the programs to work in either way (the appropriate manuals should be consulted). Data can be entered via assignment statements or through the keyboard during a RUN whenever an INPUT statement is executed. This 'conversational' form of data entry is one of the real strengths of the BASIC language. The reader may care to type in and RUN the following program, which is self explanatory (a 29% basic rate tax is assumed).

```
10 INPUT "Book price ",Price
20 Royalty = 0.075
30 Post_tax = 0.71
40 PRINT "The Author's post tax yield = £"; Price*Royalty*Post_tax
50 END
```

Notice the texts in lines 10 and 40. They are printed out exactly as they appear between their quotation marks, e.g. the space before the end quotes in line 10 is reproduced. This is an example of something included only to help legibility. The syntax of the INPUT statement in line 10 causes the computer to print a question mark when it encounters the comma! The semicolon in line 40 causes the computer to print the numeric value of the arithmetic expression immediately after the text (all the blank spaces in this algebraic expression are ignored). The 31 textual characters occupy columns 0 to 30, which explains why the requisite nine columns for the numerical solution fit onto the end of a standard 40 column screen display (i.e. columns 0 to 39 for the BBC Micro in Mode 7).

If the semicolon is replaced by a comma there will be nine empty character spaces on the text line, and the numerical solution is printed on a new line. This is a consequence of the combination of the following points: the standard number of 10 columns per print field; the allocation to successive print fields of items separated by commas in the PRINT list; and the automatic 'right justification' of numerical amounts within print fields. So the semicolon suppresses the normal separation of print items, and if a PRINT statement ends with a semicolon then this suppresses the normal line feed when the next PRINT or INPUT statement is encountered. Text is always 'left justified' and numerical output is 'right justified' within a print field.

INPUT and PRINT statements contain many traps. Distinguish carefully between zero and the letters o and O, and between 1 and the letters l, i and I. Also be careful with your response to INPUT statements; the number 2500, say, must not be entered as 2,500 which implies two separate data items of 2 and 500 respectively. However, the positioning of printed output can be controlled quite easily and precisely with the TAB function, where TAB(N) moves the print cursor to column N. This is often used in the programs which follow. It is also easy to control the scrolling action of the screen so that the user does not miss the early part of the printout—refer to your manuals for details. Some output is best viewed in an 80 column format, which can be obtained in BBC BASIC in Mode 3. BBC BASIC also allows easy control of the width of the print field and the number of decimal places. For instance, line 5 below rounds the quantities shown on the printout to the nearest penny:

```
5 @% = &02020A
```

Please consult your manuals for the details of these facilities.

1.5 Loops, conditional statements and user defined functions

A 'REPEAT UNTIL' loop is used to repeat a given action as often as necessary to satisfy a stated condition, whereas a 'FOR NEXT' loop is repeated a predetermined number of times. These loop constructions are contrasted below in equivalent programs for forming the partial sums of the roots of the integers from 1 to 10

'FOR NEXT'

```
 5 @% = &02020A
10 SUM = 0
20 FOR I = 1 TO 10
30 SUM = SUM + SQR(I)
40 PRINT I, SUM
50 NEXT I
60 END
```

'REPEAT UNTIL'

```
 5 @% = &02020A
10 I = 0 : SUM = 0
20 REPEAT
30 I = I + 1
40 SUM = SUM + SQR(I)
50 PRINT I, SUM
60 UNTIL I = 10
70 END
```

The 'FOR NEXT' version is preferable here as the programmer has decided in advance that the loop will be performed 10 times. Now suppose that we wanted the partial sums, not of the roots but of complicated functions of the integers. This can be handled easily and elegantly with user defined functions. The following amendments and additions are required.

'FOR NEXT'

```
 30 SUM = SUM + FNmole(I)
 80
 90 FNmole(X)
100 = (X + 2*X^3) / 4 - 2
```

'REPEAT UNTIL'

```
 40 SUM = SUM + FNmole(I)
 80
 90 FNmole(X)
100 = (X + 2*X^3) / 4 - 2
```

The function called mole(X) is defined in statements 90 and 100, as in statement 7010 given earlier. Lines 30 and 40 accumulate the requisite partial sums. The program structure is crystal clear, and the partial sums of any other function of the integers can be obtained simply by changing the line 100. The reader can check this by substituting the statement 100 = SQR(X) which will reproduce the earlier results.

Now suppose that the partial sums are to be performed only until a target sum of 20 is achieved or exceeded for the first time. It is only necessary to change line 60, in the 'REPEAT UNTIL' version, to achieve an efficient result. The 'FOR NEXT' version requires the use of 'IF THEN' in lines 25 and 40, and modifications to lines 10 and 20. This is inefficient as the programmer has to guess the value of the loop delimiter.

'FOR NEXT'   'REPEAT UNTIL'

```
10 SUM = 0 : TEST$ = "OK"                     60 UNTIL SUM >= 20
20 FOR I = 1 TO 400
25 IF SUM >= 20 THEN TEST$ = ""
40 IF TEST$ = "OK" THEN PRINT I, SUM
```

If your BASIC does not support 'REPEAT UNTIL' you should simulate such loops by the simple technique which is explained in the appendix to this chapter. Some BASIC dialects do not provide 'IF THEN' statements as in line 25, or in the developed form 'IF THEN ELSE'. The appendix shows how the effect of these statements can be improvised using the 'IF THEN GOTO' statement which is always available in BASIC.

1.6 Structured BASIC

The 'IF THEN' statement is used a great deal in this book, but never in the form 'IF THEN GOTO'. In fact the GOTO statement may be conditional or unconditional and it directs the execution of the program to a specified line number. Either form can wreck the presentation of a clear and logical program structure. The resulting mess, colloquially termed 'spaghetti programming', is very difficult for the programmer, let alone a third party, to read or debug. GOTO statements have been banned from this book, and the reader should seriously consider a similar resolution!

It is simpler to think of a complicated programming task in terms of its constituent parts. Arrange the detail of each part separately, and control the execution and sequencing of the parts with a 'main' program. The principle is exactly similar to that of managerial delegation of tasks to subordinates. The manager allocates and coordinates the work of subordinates, who in an ideal world would be able to work on their own tasks without interference from, but with cognizance of, the work of others. When the allocation of work is ill-considered the outcome is inefficiency and confusion; 'spaghetti management' in fact!

In structured BASIC a main program organizes a number of

separate tasks called PROCEDURES. For example, almost every program in this book has an input PROCEDURE, often called PROCinput, and an output PROCEDURE, called PROCprint. Notice the abbreviated description and the different use of upper and lower cases. PROCEDURES begin with a DEF PROC statement, as in DEF PROCinput. These may be very short, and average a dozen or so statements in this book. All PROCE-DURES end with an ENDPROC statement which instructs the computer to execute the statement after the original call of the PROCEDURE. A blank statement line is used at the start and end of each PROCEDURE to emphasize the structure of the program.

The reader who is new to structured programming will soon find the approach natural and convenient. Readers without BBC BASIC can substitute SUBROUTINES for PROCEDURES throughout the programs of this book. No extra lines are required. A descriptive REM can substitute for a DEF PROC, a RETURN for an ENDPROC, and a GOSUB for a PROCEDURE call. This is summarized below, for PROCabc.

BBC BASIC	Others
PROCabc	GOSUB L
. . .	. . .
L DEF PROCabc	L REM abc
. . .	. . .
. . .	. . .
ENDPROC	RETURN

1.7 The approach of this book to BASIC programs

This is a short book, and yet even so those sections and exercises marked with an asterisk may be omitted on a first reading. Most readers should be able to key the programs into their computers direct from the text. Write or telephone me at Loughborough University, Ashby Road, Loughborough, Leics. about the availability of disk software.

My primary aim is that the reader learns how to use BASIC for the computations of OR models. To this end the programs are as short and clear as I can make them. Thus they cannot be 'user-proof' e.g. the programs will crash if users enter unaccept-able data. It is very easy for anyone to make an error when keying in data, and the preliminary exercise in each chapter asks the user to write an edit PROCEDURE , PROCedit say, which is called immediately after PROCinput to allow the user to make any corrections to the data.

Professional computer software is generally 'packaged' in a sophisticated way. But limited space and my educational objectives disallow such refinements as menu driven options, file handling, elaborate colour graphics, use of sound, error trapping, etc. If the book succeeds in its primary aim then the readers should not have too much difficulty with doing such development themselves!

1.8 References

1. Alcock, D., *Illustrating BASIC*, Cambridge University Press (1977).
2. Freeman, R., *Step by Step BASIC*, Lifelong Learning Ltd, Cambridge (1983).
3. Freeman, R., *Structured BASIC*, BBC Publications, London (1984).

1.9 Appendix

This appendix shows how to simulate 'REPEAT UNTIL' loops and 'IF THEN' structures using primitive BASIC dialects (after Freeman, ref. 3).

BBC BASIC	Some other BASICs
| ```
45   REPEAT

     ::::::

     ::::::

115 UNTIL N = 0
``` | ```
45 FOR I = 0 TO 1
46 I = 1

::::::

::::::

113 IF N <> 0 THEN I = 0
115 NEXT I
``` |

The converse of the condition following the UNTIL can always be used in the line preceding NEXT I in order to return the loop counter I to its initial value. If the 'other BASIC' does not support 'IF THEN' in the form of line 113 then this must be amended and an extra statement is required on line 114 as follows:

```
113 IF N=0 THEN GOTO 115
114 I = 0
```

You can simulate 'IF THEN ELSE' with similar techniques.

Chapter 2

Introduction to business operations research

2.1 Introduction

Formal definitions are often cumbersome, pedantic and verbose. For example, the Operations Research Society of America states that

> Operations Research is concerned with scientifically deciding how to best design and operate man–machine systems, usually requiring the allocation of scarce resources.

This is not much improved by the longer definition given by the Operational Research Society of Great Britain:

> Operational Research is the application of the methods of science to complex problems arising in the direction and management of large systems of men, machines, materials and money in industry, business, government and defence. The distinctive approach is to develop a scientific model of the system, incorporating measurements of factors such as chance and risk, with which to predict and compare the outcomes of alternative decisions, strategies and controls. The purpose is to help management determine its policy and actions scientifically.

The terms 'Business Operations Research' (Operational Research) and 'Management Science' have come to mean essentially the same thing: the systematic study of management issues emphasizing quantitative analysis of interrelating factors. Quantitative studies typically suggest directions for the improved allocation of resources. Any facet of business may be involved, and it is not unusual for a project team to act as 'honest brokers' when thinking through the benefits to the organization as a whole of changes in the functions and status of separate departments or divisions.

The basis of operations research (OR) is the belief that, in the long run, the use of formal quantitative analyses will lead to decisions which are significantly better than those based solely on experience and intuition. How far this is so in a given situation will depend upon very many factors. If the outcomes are fairly obvious then there may be no need to use formal analysis to decide on the best decision. OR is least likely to be appropriate in a fast-moving, creative environment where immediate decisions are required to constantly changing problems. But OR may be essential when a key decision is to be made in a measured and deliberate way, especially if considerable capital sums are involved or the decision seems likely to affect the work of a substantial part of an organization. On the other hand, the fruits of an OR study can also lead to efficient ways of dealing with repetitive decisions which might have consumed a disproportionate share of a manager's time.

An OR study is commonly initiated by a manager who calls upon the services of an OR group. OR personnel may be included within a management services department or contracted for the duration of the project from an external management consultancy. It is normal practice to form a project team including members of the company with a wide range of skills and experience. These may be mathematicians, computer and data processing professionals, financial and line managers, etc.

Quite apart from the competence of the members of the project team in their own fields, there are the dominant influences of the political environment, and the culture of the organization. The technical analysis could be first rate, but it would be naive to look forward to the successful implementation of well-founded recommendations if a study does not come at a propitious time, or it is not actively supported by senior management.

The organizational culture will have an important effect upon the 'observation' of the system under study, which is the very first stage of any scientific investigation. If each department of a company, say, is permitted or encouraged by the Board to take an insular attitude, then it will not be realistic to expect the easy identification of opportunities covering more than a single department.

The ideal context for OR to show its full value is when a numerate and skilful manager has identified an endemic problem as suitable for quantitative analysis, and has then won support for a systemic appraisal from colleagues as well as senior management. Confidence is then engendered at the start of the OR work that if a sound set of recommendations is presented then they will be implemented.

The project team has to decide on the scope of the study. Scope must be wide enough to allow the organization to make a substantial step forward and to satisfy the commissioning manager, but not so wide as to prejudice the successful implementation of the recommendations. For instance, it might be unwise to extend the boundaries of the study beyond the sphere of control, or influence, of the 'sponsoring' decision maker. The conclusion of this stage will be an agreement on the detailed terms of reference. Considerable diplomacy may be required if the preliminary study by the project team provides a view of the problem too far removed from the initial view of the sponsor.

2.2 Mathematical modelling

A mathematical model is used to formalize the 'causal mechanisms' which link outcomes to the factors under the control of the sponsor. What, for example, are the consequences for the sales of established products in the years to come if the current pattern of dispersed distribution warehouses is replaced by a few strategically located distribution centres? Changes in the physical distribution resources employed by the company can be costed by a suitable quantitative analysis, and a change is likely to have an influence on the pricing strategy. Suppose that the sales force adopts a system of taking customers' orders against delivery on a 'nominated day', which depends upon the location of the customer within a large delivery region. What effect will this have on customers who have been used to placing orders for delivery at their own convenience? Would a computer system for scheduling delivery vehicles save money and improve service levels? What are the sales implications of a schedule of price discounts, based on quantity delivered, and in particular the imposition for the first time of a minimum order quantity? Should the opportunity be taken to reorganize the sales force to acknowledge the range of differing customers? How 'elastic' are sales levels to the perception by customers of 'service', and indeed, what are the determinants of 'service'?

Causal mechanisms must be researched to the point where quantified relationships can be used to describe the interplay of 'decision variables' such as the shape of the new distribution network, the largely uncontrollable variables such as maximum vehicle speeds and general environmental factors such as the likely response of competitors.

A mathematical model entails a coherent set of (usually algebraic) relationships suitable for the purpose on hand. It is an abstraction of reality which puts the complexities of the real situation into a logical and structured form which is amenable to analysis. A good model is as simple as possible, partly for reasons of economy in construction, and partly because simple models are usually easier to solve.

If a solution of the model at first defies the analytical prowess of those involved then a number of technical simplifications can be introduced. Variables can be aggregated into broader classes, so that differentiation is between classes of product rather than individual product lines. Non-linear numerical relationships may be replaced by piecewise linear relationships, in which proportionality at a given rate is assumed over a restricted range of activity. One could decompose a complex model of a large system into a number of separate models of particular aspects. For instance, the delivery cost relationships for a decision about the number and location of distribution centres may be much less detailed than is required in a model to relate delivery costs to the imposition of minimum delivery quantities. Again, a model which looked at the next ten years' business can be separated into models for the immediate prospect and the long-term outlook. The construction of models calls for experience just as much as technical proficiency. Successful modelling is the art of the possible.

It may be natural to doubt whether a given model represents the real situation in an adequate way. Shortcomings cannot always be removed by elaboration. There may be problems with collecting basic data in the form and volume required. Indeed, some data may be unavailable or too costly to obtain. There will also be computational restrictions. The more comprehensive the model the more difficult it may be to obtain a forecast of outcomes to changes in decision variables. Furthermore, elaboration of a model can be very costly and take valuable time.

The validation of the model is very important, and yet it may be difficult. Fresh data will be required to test the performance of parts of the model, but, if the model is being used to project the consequences of future decisions, then there may be no wholly satisfactory way of validating the performance of the model as a whole in the absence of information which can be obtained only after a proposed change has been implemented. If the model is to be used purely to describe the *status quo* then validation should be much less problematic.

Once a model has been validated to the satisfaction of the project team it may be employed for its designed purpose. It is important to realize that the computational results must be interpreted in the context of the problem, and it is rarely if ever the case that the recommendations of the project team conform exactly to the 'optimum' solution from the model. There may be a multitude of qualitative factors which will be used to assess the outputs. But this is no criticism, rather an understanding of the need to balance quantitative and qualitative approaches.

The project team will experiment with the model to learn about the significance of variations in some of the key decision variables. How sensitive is the proposed solution to minor errors or changes in the data? Does an examination of the results suggest that further conceptual developments should be fed back into the initial assessment? Have there been important changes in the team's outlook as a result of learning more about the problem on the basis of the experimental results? The team will also want to explore the robustness of any supposedly 'optimum' solution from the model to changing circumstances. Does the minimum cost solution, for example, suggest a highly unconventional form of distribution network which would be quite incapable of handling different classes of product or unsuitable for alternative marketing arrangements? Is there a fundamental difference between the shape of the distribution network which would reduce the operating costs over ten years to a minimum, as opposed to the distribution network which would maximize the rate of return on investment? What if the planned changes from current practice came to a halt before complete implementation of the plan?

The potential benefits of modelling can be so important that in some of the larger companies the management trainees are encouraged to work for OR teams in order to absorb the process of OR and the company culture, before taking up management positions.

2.3 Microcomputers and business operations research

Microcomputers have had a major 'enabling' influence on the pursuit of OR. In the first place OR professionals can have the smaller scale computational work under their own direct control, and are no longer dependent upon large machines operated either by data processing departments or expensive computer bureaux. There is some evidence that the use of micros has reduced the time required for model development and validation.

Micros are also cheap enough and simple enough for them to be used by the sponsors on a routine basis when the model is completed. For example, the personnel department might have a need for a manpower planning model which projects staffing levels into the future, given reasonable assumptions about the levels of resignations and promotions. Such a model could be run as a routine on a micro located in the personnel department in order to assist with recruitment decisions.

The advanced graphics facilities of micros can be utilized to improve the standard of communication between the project team and the sponsors of the project. This is not only true of the use of charts, graphs and figures for descriptive statistics. It is particularly true of the use of animated graphics employed in simulation studies. These techiques help the less numerate and more apprehensive individuals come to appreciate the modelling effort and contribute to the experimental phase of 'what if' modelling.

There are many user-friendly software packages for micros, such as 'spreadsheets', which enable some forms of numerical analysis to be conducted relatively effortlessly. This has been warmly welcomed by OR groups. It is also noted that accountants, for example, are using spreadsheets for financial modelling problems such as cash flow forecasts, and engineers are conducting their own capital investment appraisals. However, the use of software packages is outside the scope of this volume.

Networked micros also offer considerably enlarged potential for OR work. For example, a micro can be used to log data at remote locations for transmission to another micro at a later date. Micros can also be used to interrogate and update the data held on a central database. The term 'Management Information System' (MIS) is in vogue for describing a computer system in which an 'intelligent terminal' provides a manager with the information which he or she requires in order to plan ahead. To do this, raw data must be processed in some way and presented in a suitable form, providing further scope for mathematical modelling. The next chapter, for example, describes the manipulation of sales data to provide a set of indices of sales volumes and prices.

2.4 The approach of this book to business operations research

This book is designed to fill the gap between texts on 'the management application of computers' and texts on 'operational research techniques'. It cannot hope to present balanced accounts either of the art of mathematical modelling or of OR techniques in the space available. Instead I have made a selection from the core curriculum of standardized models and have unavoidably neglected the creative side of modelling.

The content is graded so that the numerate reader who is new to OR should be able to follow all of the material on index numbers in Chapter 3, and most of the material on data fitting in Chapter 4. Chapter 5 should be accessible to most readers and demonstrates the potential of combining the graphics facilities of modern micros with mathematical modelling in the context of project management networks. Chapter 6 and 7 would be harder going for the reader who is new to linear programming and Markov chains.

There are a growing number of micro software packages for

standardized modelling in the fields of investment appraisal, critical path networks, and linear programming, etc. These are mainly marketed for the professional OR analyst to use in a commercial setting, but they may be poorly documented and difficult to tailor for specific purposes. The programs of this book have an educational purpose, but they may be useful in small scale OR work.

Four references to excellent books are given below for the interested reader.

2.5 References

1. Anderson, D. R., Sweeney, D. J. and Williams, T. A., *An Introduction to Management Science* (4th ed.), West Publishing Co. (1985).
2. Daellenbach, H. G. and George, J. A., *Introduction to Operations Research Techniques*, Allyn and Bacon (1978)
3. White, D. J., *Operational Research*, Wiley (1985)
4. Williams, H. P., *Model Building in Mathematical Programming* (2nd ed.), Wiley (1985)

Chapter 3

Index numbers

Essential theory

Index numbers are widely used by government agencies, trade organizations, public bodies and companies of all sizes. The elementary material on index numbers is developed here in the context of sales turnover, and then employees' reports. The elementary material on composite indices is developed in the context of company sales figures. The reader should bear in mind the applicability of the ideas across the spectra of activities which are amenable to quantitative measurement, in commerce, industry and the public sector.

3.1 Indices based on simple relatives*

The significance of a percentage change in sales turnover may be readily assimilated. A reported sales increase of 12 per cent has immediate impact. The value of a 'year end' sales index of 112 based on an index of 100 at the start of the year conveys the same information just as readily.

Suppose that management is interested in monitoring sales turnover in the face of the launch of a product by competitors. It would be sensible to 'base' a sales index of 100 upon the sales in the period immediately preceding the launch. This choice would clearly show up any sales trends that might develop. The first row of Table 3.1 provides a series of actual monthly sales figures, where month 0 is the base month. It is seen that within three or

Table 3.1 Sales turnover

Month	i		0	1	2	3	4	5	6	7	8
Sales (£000's)	S_i		300	305	306	282	258	190	310	329	350
Sales index	I_i	(1)	100	102	102	94	86	63	103	110	117
% increase		(2)		2	0	–8	–9	–26	63	6	6
Chain index	I'	(3)		1.02	1.00	0.92	0.91	0.74	1.63	1.06	1.06

Notes: (1) From $I = S_i/S_0 \times 100$.
(2) Month on month percentage increases in sales S to the nearest integer.
(3) From $I'_{i-1,i} = S_i/S_{i-1}$.

*Relatives are ratios in this context.

17

four months the rival product starts to make serious inroads into sales turnover, which is then restored and eventually enhanced (possibly by a vigorous promotional campaign).

The sales index I_i for month i, as shown in the third line of the table, is calculated from

$$I_i = \frac{\text{Sales turnover in month } i}{\text{Sales turnover in base month}} \times 100 = S_i/S_0 \times 100$$

where S_i denotes the sales turnover in month i.

The ratio S_i/S_0 is an example of a simple (i.e. unweighted) 'relative'. The numerical value of the sales index I_i shows how sales turnover in month i compares to 'base turnover' in the base month (i.e. month 0). This sales index is given in line three of the table rounded to the nearest integer. There was a substantial drop in sales in months 4 and 5 prior to a strong recovery from month 6 onwards.

The table also shows the month-on-month percentage changes in sales levels: these figures can be important, as when the remuneration of the sales force is tied to the monthly changes in sales turnover! The same information can be expressed in index form: the so-called chain index I' is given by

$$I'_{i-1,i} = \frac{\text{Sales turnover in month } i}{\text{Sales turnover in month } i-1} = S_i/S_{i-1}$$

Notice that the chain index I' is the ratio of sales in successive months. It is not difficult to see that the product of chain indices is closely related to the sales index I. Thus

$$I'_{0,1} \times I'_{1,2} \times I'_{2,3} \times \ldots \times I'_{i-1,i}$$
$$= S_1/S_0 \times S_2/S_1 \times S_3/S_2 \times \ldots \times S_i/S_{i-1} = S_i/S_0 = I_i/100$$

This identity should be employed with caution. For example

$$I'_{0,1} \times I'_{1,2} \times I'_{2,3} \times I'_{3,4} = 1.02 \times 1.00 \times 0.92 \times 0.91 = 0.85$$

There is a disparity in the second decimal place between this and the value of $I_4/100 = 0.86$ shown in the table. Chain indices are not in common use in industry partly because of this sort of problem; on the other hand, many government indices are based around similar, but further elaborated, ideas.

Program SIMPREL, below, calculates an index based on a simple relative and it also calculates a period-on-period chain index. The simple main program sequences the following PROCEDURES:

PROCinput:	allows the user to input the base period B, and the final period N together with the data DAT(I) for periods I = B, ..., N.
PROCsimple__relative:	calculates the index INDEX(I) for the simple relative DAT(I)/DAT(B) * 100 and tabulates these values for I = B, ..., N to the nearest integer.
PROCchain:	calculates the chain index CHINDEX(I) from DAT(I)/DAT(I−1) for each I = B+1, . . . ,N and tabulates these values rounded to the second decimal place.

Type in this program from the listing below.

Program 3.1 SIMPREL: Index of simple relatives

```
  10 REM SIMPREL
  20 REM INDEX OF SIMPLE RELATIVES
  30 REM ALSO PROVIDES CHAIN INDICES
  40 DIM DAT(100),INDEX(100),CHINDEX(100)
  50
  60 PROCinput
  70 PROCsimple_relative
  80 PROCchain
  90 END
 100
1000 DEF PROCinput
1010 PRINT "ENTER ALL DATA NUMERICALLY"
1020 INPUT "BASE PERIOD ",B
1030 INPUT "FINAL PERIOD ",N
1040 PRINT : PRINT "PERIOD    DATA"
1050 FOR I= B TO N
1060 PRINT TAB(0);I; : INPUT TAB(10) DAT(I)
1070 NEXT I
1080 ENDPROC
1090
2000 DEF PROCsimple_relative
2010 PRINT : PRINT
2020 PRINT "PERIOD    INDEX OF"
2030 PRINT TAB(10) "SIMPLE RELATIVES"
2040 FOR I=B TO N
2050 INDEX(I)=DAT(I)/DAT(B)*100
2060 INDEX(I)=INT(INDEX(I)+.5)
2070 PRINT TAB(0);I,INDEX(I)
2080 NEXT I
2090 ENDPROC
2100
3000 DEF PROCchain
3010 PRINT : PRINT
3020 PRINT "PERIOD    CHAIN INDEX"
3030 FOR I=B+1 TO N
3040 CHINDEX(I)=DAT(I)/DAT(I-1)
3050 CHINDEX(I)=INT(CHINDEX(I)*100+.5)
3060 PRINT TAB(0);I,CHINDEX(I)/100
3070 NEXT I
3080 ENDPROC
```

RUN this program with the data from the first two lines of Table 3.1. You should find that your output corresponds to the third and final row of Table 3.1. ReRUN with data of your own choice, but notice that because the arrays have been dimensioned to 100 in line 40 you should enter 1985, for example, as 85.

```
RUN
ENTER ALL DATA NUMERICALLY
BASE PERIOD ?0
FINAL PERIOD ?8

PERIOD    DATA
0         300
1         305
2         306
3         282
4         258
5         190
6         310
7         329
8         350

PERIOD    INDEX OF
          SIMPLE RELATIVES
0             100
1             102
2             102
3              94
4              86
5              63
6             103
7             110
8             117

PERIOD    CHAIN INDEX
1             1.02
2             1
3             0.92
4             0.91
5             0.74
6             1.63
7             1.06
8             1.06
```

Now do Problems 3.1 to 3.3 at the end of this chapter.

3.2 Deflators

Suppose that annual sales data is available for a span of several years, as in Table 3.2. One could use program SIMPREL to find the sales indices in monetary terms. However, the expression of sales turnover in real terms, which allowed for inflationary effects, might have much greater importance.

National statistics include many 'deflator' series for use in a variety of circumstances, from the most general to the highly specific. The reader is almost certainly familiar with the announcements of movements in the General Index of Retail Prices (RPI) in the media: at the time of writing, the RPI is projected to reach an average value of 282 for 1986 from a base of

100 in 1975. This is an instance of a *composite* index which is designed to summarize changes in the overall price of a 'package' of retail goods as experienced by an 'average' consumer. It has achieved a measure of general (often unquestioning) acceptance on both sides of industry for a variety of purposes, including wage bargaining.

If the sales data of Table 3.2 relate to part-time earnings, say of a tradesman in his spare time, then the RPI could well be appropriate for adjusting these earnings to real rather than monetary values. The RPI is shown in line 4 of Table 3.2.

Another very important national statistic is that known as the 'Implied Deflator of the Gross Domestic Product at Market Prices' (GDP); this roughly doubled over the five years from 1975 to 1980. This index is imputed from the ratio of GDP at current values/GDP in real values. The reader is referred elsewhere (see *The National Accounts – a short guide*, by H. Copeman, 1981, HMSO) for a technical definition and an authoritative statement of the interpretation and use of this series. But in so far as a company contributes in a general way to the gross domestic product then the GDP series does provide a reasonable basis for adjustment of sales turnover to real rather than monetary values. This index is shown in line 3 of Table 3.2.

Table 3.2 Sales turnover and deflator series

Year i	1975	1976	1977	1978	1979	1980	1981	1982	1983
Sales S_i	498	563	658	781	933	1203	1381	1572	1790
GDP deflator[1]	50.2	57.6	65.6	72.9	83.5	100	111.7	119.6	125.7
RPI deflator[2]	100	116.5	135.0	146.2	165.8	195.6	218.9	237.7	248.6
Sales index[3]	100	113	132	157	187	242	277	316	359
Real sales index[4]	100	99	101	108	113	121	125	132	144
Real sales index[5]	100	97	98	107	113	124	127	133	145

Notes: (1) From Table 1.16. UK National Accounts 1984. HMSO.
　　　　(2) From Table 114. Economic Trends Annual Supplement 1984. HMSO.
　　　　(3) Based on a simple relative $S_i/S_0 \times 100$.
　　　　(4) Based on (3) deflated by the GDP deflator (1).
　　　　(5) Based on (3) deflated by the RPI deflator (2).

If we denote by D_i a deflator index in year i then the sales turnover S_i in that year can be deflated to real terms RS_i in year 0 values as follows

$$RS_i = S_i \times D_0/D_i$$

Consequently the index of real sales turnover RI_i is given by

$$RI_i = RS_i/RS_0 \times 100 = I_i\, D_0/D_i$$

It is not difficult to modify program SIMPREL in order to produce indices in real rather than monetary terms, as follows.

Amend the following lines (but note that statement 50 is a specific BBC print control statement, which in this instance rounds all printed values to the nearest integer. Users of other micros should use the technique in lines 2060 and 3050 of Program SIMPREL):

```
10 REM DEFLATR
20 REM INDEX OF SIMPLE RELATIVES
30 REM WITH AND WITHOUT DEFLATOR
40 DIM DAT(100),INDEX(100),D(100)
50 @%=&0002000A

80 PROCdeflate
```

DELETE 2060
DELETE 3000 to 3080

Now type in PROCdeflate which allows the user to input a deflator series, and then prints the deflated index of simple relatives.

Program 3.2 DEFLATR: Indices with and without deflator series

```
  10 REM DEFLATR
  20 REM INDEX OF SIMPLE RELATIVES
  30 REM WITH AND WITHOUT DEFLATOR
  40 DIM DAT(100),INDEX(100),D(100)
  50 @%=&0002000A
  60 PROCinput
  70 PROCsimple_relative
  80 PROCdeflate
  90 END
 100
1000 DEF PROCinput
1010 PRINT "ENTER ALL DATA NUMERICALLY"
1020 INPUT "BASE PERIOD ",B
1030 INPUT "FINAL PERIOD ",N
1040 PRINT : PRINT "PERIOD      DATA"
1050 FOR I= B TO N
1060 PRINT TAB(0);I; : INPUT TAB(10) DAT(I)
1070 NEXT I
1080 ENDPROC
1090
2000 DEF PROCsimple_relative
2010 PRINT : PRINT
2020 PRINT "PERIOD      INDEX OF"
2030 PRINT TAB(10) "SIMPLE RELATIVES"
2040 FOR I=B TO N
2050 INDEX(I)=DAT(I)/DAT(B)*100
2070 PRINT TAB(0);I,INDEX(I)
2080 NEXT I
2090 ENDPROC
2100
4000 DEF PROCdeflate
4010 PRINT : PRINT : PRINT "NOW ENTER THE DEFLATOR SERIES "
4020 PRINT "PERIOD      DEFLATOR"
4030 FOR I= B TO N
4040 PRINT TAB(0);I; : INPUT TAB(10) D(I)
4050 IF I>B THEN D(I)=D(I)/D(B)
4060 NEXT I : D(B)=1
4070 PRINT : PRINT : PRINT "SERIES IN REAL TERMS"
4080 PRINT "PERIOD      BASE ";B;TAB(20) "BASE ";N
4090 PRINT TAB(10) "=100";TAB(20) "=100"
4100 PRINT
4110 FOR I=B TO N
4120 INDEXb=INDEX(I)/D(I)
4130 INDEXn=INDEXb/INDEX(N)*D(N)*100
4140 PRINT TAB(0);I;TAB(10) INDEXb;TAB(20) INDEXn
4150 NEXT I
4160 ENDPROC
```

RUN
ENTER ALL DATA NUMERICALLY
BASE PERIOD ?75
FINAL PERIOD ?83

PERIOD	DATA
75.	498
76.	563
77.	658
78.	781
79.	933
80.	1203
81.	1381
82.	1572
83.	1790

PERIOD	INDEX OF SIMPLE RELATIVES
75.	100.
76.	113.
77.	132.
78.	157.
79.	187.
80.	242.
81.	277.
82.	316.
83.	359.

NOW ENTER THE DEFLATOR SERIES

PERIOD	DEFLATOR
75.	50.2
76.	57.6
77.	65.6
78.	72.9
79.	83.5
80.	100
81.	111.7
82.	119.6
83.	125.7

SERIES IN REAL TERMS

PERIOD	BASE 75. =100	BASE 83. =100
75.	100.	70.
76.	99.	69.
77.	101.	70.
78.	108.	75.
79.	113.	78.
80.	121.	84.
81.	125.	87.
82.	132.	92.
83.	144.	100.

RUN
ENTER ALL DATA NUMERICALLY
BASE PERIOD ?75
FINAL PERIOD ?83

PERIOD	DATA
75.	498
76.	563
77.	658
78.	781
79.	933
80.	1203
81.	1381
82.	1572
83.	1790

PERIOD	INDEX OF SIMPLE RELATIVES
75.	100.
76.	113.
77.	132.
78.	157.
79.	187.
80.	242.
81.	277.
82.	316.
83.	359.

NOW ENTER THE DEFLATOR SERIES

PERIOD	DEFLATOR
75.	100
76.	116.5
77.	135.0
78.	146.2
79.	165.8
80.	195.6
81.	218.9
82.	237.7
83.	248.6

SERIES IN REAL TERMS

PERIOD	BASE 75. =100	BASE 83. =100
75.	100.	69.
76.	97.	67.
77.	98.	68.
78.	107.	74.
79.	113.	78.
80.	124.	85.
81.	127.	88.
82.	133.	92.
83.	145.	100.

Now check your listing against that for Program DEFLATR above. When satisfied with the accuracy of your listing you should RUN with the data of Table 3.2 above. Note that the years should be entered as double digits, so enter 1975 as 75. The output of a RUN with the GDP deflator should resemble the series in the penultimate row of Table 3.2, and the output of a second RUN using the RPI deflator in the final row.

There is a marked similarity between the indices deflated both by the RPI and the GDP deflators. The overall conclusion must be that the apparent 250 per cent increase in monetary sales turnover shrinks to much less than a 50 per cent increase in real terms. It seems highly questionable whether the majority of UK firms even today routinely interpret their sales figures in this way, despite the crucial need to have done so during the period under investigation here.

3.3 Employees' reports

It is now standard practice for many of the larger companies to circulate annual 'Employees' Reports'. This is done partly to foster an interest in the trajectory of the business, and partly to engender positive attitudes to profitable operation. Figures are usually quoted, on a *per capita* basis, under the heads shown in Figure 3.1 (although the use of the possibly emotive head 'operating profit' is often avoided).

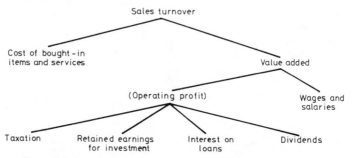

Figure 3.1 Accounting structure of a conventional employees' report

The style of reporting is chosen to emphasize the importance of value added concepts, so that wage bargaining is less likely to be based on crude operating profitability. The figures are usually expressed in real terms if comparisons are made with previous years.

Suppose then that we have the same sales turnover figures from Table 3.2, but that in addition the data on the number of employees N_i is available (in some appropriate units). One could 'deflate' the monetary sales turnover figures S_i by the number of employees N_i before deflating once more by the GDP deflator. But it seems easier here to modify program DEFLATR to form the ratio S_i/N_i on data input. Make the following alterations:

```
1060 PRINT TAB(0); I; : INPUT TAB(10) s, n
1065 DAT(I) = s/n
```

Now RUN this amended program for the data in rows two to four of Table 3.3 as shown below. Notice that you must enter the sales turnover value, a comma, and the number of employees for the data input in each period. This RUN is given after Table 3.3.

Table 3.3   Sales turnover per employee

Year	1975	1976	1977	1978	1979	1980	1981	1982	1983
Sales turnover	498	563	658	781	933	1203	1381	1572	1790
Employees	25	28	34	35	35	35	35	34	34
GDP deflator(1)	50.2	57.6	65.6	72.9	83.5	100	111.7	119.6	125.7
Sales per employee(2)	100	101	97	112	134	173	198	232	264
Real sales per employee(3)	100	88	74	77	80	87	89	97	106

Notes: (1) From Table 1.16 UK National Accounts 1984, HMSO.
      (2) Index of sales turnover per employee.
      (3) Index of real sales turnover per employee deflated by (1).

```
RUN
ENTER ALL DATA NUMERICALLY
BASE PERIOD ?75
FINAL PERIOD ?83

PERIOD     DATA
75.        498,25
76.        563,28
77.        658,34
78.        781,35
79.        933,35
80.        1203,35
81.        1381,35
82.        1572,34
83.        1790,34


PERIOD     INDEX OF
           SIMPLE RELATIVES
75.            100.
76.            101.
77.             97.
78.            112.
79.            134.
80.            173.
81.            198.
82.            232.
83.            264.


NOW ENTER THE DEFLATOR SERIES
PERIOD     DEFLATOR
75.        50.2
76.        57.6
77.        65.6
78.        72.9
79.        83.5
80.        100.
81.        111.7
82.        119.6
83.        125.7
```

```
SERIES IN REAL TERMS
PERIOD    BASE 75.   BASE 83.
          =100       =100

75.       100.       95.
76.       88.        83.
77.       74.        70.
78.       77.        73.
79.       80.        76.
80.       87.        82.
81.       89.        84.
82.       97.        92.
83.       106.       100.
```

Quite obviously the company has suffered very badly from over-recruiting; the number of employees increased in rough proportion to the monetary sales turnover from 1975 to 1977. Sales per employee in real terms had slumped by 1977 to around three-quarters of the 1975 value, therafter creeping upward and only passing the 1975 value for the first time by 1983. This example illustrates the importance of manpower planning based on quantitative data.

Value added is the difference between sales turnover S_i and the cost C_i of bought-in materials and services: it is sometimes used as a proxy for productivity in the service sector. High levels of value added *per capita* in real terms is directly in the interests of both the company shareholders and employees, providing both the operating profit and the wages and salaries bill as shown in Figure 3.1. Since the wages and salaries W_i cannot be significantly altered in the short term, without the appalling social costs of unemployment, the containment and reduction of costs C_i attracts top priority. A RUN of modified DEFLATR with the C_i, N_i and GDP deflator data from Table 3.4 would give an index of real costs. Likewise, a RUN of modified DEFLATR with W_i, N_i and the GDP deflator from Table 3.4 would give an index of real wages per employee, as shown.

Table 3.4   Added value, wages and salaries, and operating profit

Year	1975	1976	1977	1978	1979	1980	1981	1982	1983
Sales turnover S_i	498	563	658	781	933	1203	1381	1572	1790
Costs C_i	415	456	493	588	718	942	1040	1217	1404
Wages and salaries W_i	73	101	160	189	213	259	287	282	292
Employees N_i	25	28	34	35	35	35	35	34	34
GDP deflator(1)	50.2	57.6	65.6	72.9	83.5	100	111.7	119.6	125.7
Real indices per employee deflated by the GDP deflator:									
Costs	100	86	67	70	74	81	80	91	99
Value added	100	100	112	114	111	113	132	132	137
Wages	100	108	123	127	125	127	126	119	117
Operating profit	100	47	28	20	9	7	173	225	276

Notes: (1) From Table 1.16 UK National Accounts 1984, HMSO.

The company was most successful in reducing the real costs of bought-in materials and services just when this was most needed. The effect on the real value added per employee can be seen by modifying DEFLATR as follows

```
1060 PRINT TAB(0);I; : INPUT TAB(10) s, c, n
1065 DAT(I) = (s - c)/n
```

A RUN of this program gives the required output, as shown in Table 3.4, provided that the data is input as sales, costs, employees (i.e. S_i, C_i, N_i separated by commas for each period). The reader may care to take this on trust to avoid the tedium of data entry. Similar comments apply to the modification below, designed to produce the index of real operating profit per employee on input of sales, costs, wages and employee numbers (i.e. S_i, C_i, W_i, N_i):

```
1060 PRINT TAB(0); I;: INPUT TAB(10) s, c, w, n
1065 DAT(I) = (s - c)/n - w/n
```

The company remained profitable, if only just, because real value added increased steadily and the index of real wages followed a typical pattern for the period. Real recovery in operating profits was finally obtained, but it should not be assumed that this was distributed *in toto* to the shareholders! Figure 3.1 shows that operating profit must also provide for taxation, interest on loans, and for reinvestment. It would seem likely that dividends continued to fall in real terms and that the company has survived to mount a long overdue programme of investment — but that is another story.

3.4 Composite indices

Annual sales turnover is an aggregate of figures for sales volume across the range of a company's marketable output. It is often important for top management not only to assimilate summary statistics of total sales values but also to appreciate whether any changes are due to pricing or volume variations. Several composite 'price' and 'quantity' indices are in use for this purpose. This section describes the construction of two common types of composite indices which are based on the following idea:

$$\text{Price index} = \Sigma p_i q_{\text{ref}} / \Sigma p_0 q_{\text{ref}} \times 100$$
$$\text{Quantity index} = \Sigma q_i p_{\text{ref}} / \Sigma q_0 p_{\text{ref}} \times 100$$

where p_i is the price in period i of a 'product'
q_i is the quantity sold in period i of a 'product'
the summation is over all the products involved
the index $_0$ indicates the base period
the index $_{\text{ref}}$ indicates the reference period.

Note that the roles of the price and quantity variables interchange as between the price and quantity indices. Consequently it will suffice to describe only one of them in detail. It must be assumed that price and quantity data exist for each separately identifiable 'product' (or class of products) which together make up the marketable output to which a chosen index relates.

Take the composite price index for the purpose of further discussion. Such indices attempt to measure price changes by holding the quantity data numerically equal to that experienced in a reference period. The numerator is the numerical value of the sales of all products in period i if reference period quantities were to be sold at period i prices. The demoninator is the numerical value of the sales of all products in reference period quantities but at base period prices.

There are two well-known extreme cases for the choice of reference period. A Laspeyres price index L_p is obtained where the reference period is the base period *per se*. A Paasche price index P_p is obtained where the reference period is the current period.

Laspeyres price index $Lp_i = \Sigma p_i q_0 / \Sigma p_0 q_0 \times 100$
Paasche price index $Pp_i = \Sigma p_i q_i / \Sigma p_0 q_i \times 100$

The corresponding quantity indices L_q and P_q are obtained by interchanging the $_p$ and $_q$ in these expressions.

The Laspeyres price index has the great advantage of producing the longest comparable series, always provided that quantity variables are more or less static. It is the simplest and least demanding of data, but the assumption of base period reference becomes untenable if the quantity variables evolve rapidly. For instance, price changes may partially determine the quantities sold: a Laspeyres price index could lead to an overestimate of price inflation if less is sold as prices rise.

At the other extreme, the use of current period quantities in the Paasche index involves the collection of price and quantity data in each period. The use of the current period quantities also means that one cannot, strictly speaking, relate movements in this index exclusively to price changes. Furthermore, the introduction of new products creates problems. In practice one might choose to update a reference period somewhat infrequently so that the series resembles a Laspeyres rather than a Paasche index.

The geometric mean of the Laspeyres and Paasche price indices, known as the Ideal Price Index ID_p, has some attractive theoretical properties although it is not in common use.

$IDp_i = (Lp_i \times Pp_i)^{1/2}$

The product of price and quantity indices correctly provides the sales index $= \Sigma v_i/\Sigma v_0 = \Sigma p_i q_i/\Sigma p_0 q_0$ only in the case of the Ideal indices. If an ideal index based on 100 in the base year reaches 200 in the current year, then an alternative choice of base year in the current year would lead to 50 in the base year. Neither Laspeyres nor Paasche indices have the same desirable properties. The use of the microcomputer obviously alleviates the computational burden, which has been one objection to the use of the Ideal index in the past. But the heavy cost of data collection remains, as does the problem of dealing with a changing product mix.

Data on four classes of product are provided in Table 3.5 below. Price and quantity sold are given for each of nine periods.

Table 3.5 Monthly sales data for four products

Product		0	1	2	3	4	5	6	7	8
1	Unit price	0.8	0.9	0.7	0.8	0.9	0.7	0.8	0.9	0.7
	Quantity	100	110	100	105	115	110	115	125	111
2	Unit price	25	25	25	25	25	25	25	25	25
	Quantity	2.0	2.3	2.7	2.9	3.1	3.2	3.1	3.0	2.9
3	Unit price	12	12	11	11	10	10	10	9	9
	Quantity	6.1	6.0	6.0	5.7	5.8	5.5	5.6	5.7	5.8
4	Unit price	3	3.2	3.6	3.8	4.0	4.0	4.0	4.0	4.0
	Quantity	30	32	33	34	34	36	37	38	39
Price indices										
Laspeyres Lp		100	105	101	106	109	103	106	107	101
Paasche Pp		100	106	101	107	110	104	107	109	103
Ideal IDp		100	106	101	106	110	103	107	108	102
Quantity indices										
Laspeyres Lq		100	107	109	111	116	117	119	122	119
Paasche Pq		100	107	109	112	117	118	120	124	122
Ideal IDq		100	107	109	112	117	117	119	123	120
Value index										
$\Sigma p_i q_i/\Sigma p_0 q_0$		100	113	110	119	128	121	127	133	122

It is not easy to say what overall movements have occurred in prices, quantities or sales values by inspection of the data, and it is impossible for more than, say, a dozen products. A computer program INDICES follows for the calculation of the composite indices described in this section and shown in Table 3.5. A short main program is dimensioned for up to 10 products but this is easily enlarged as required.

PROCinput: allows the user to enter the base period B and the final period N, and the number of products PR for which a composite index is required. The user supplies price and quantity data DATp(pr,I) and DATq(pr,I) for each product pr = 1, 2, . . . ,PR and period I = B, . . . , N.

PROCindices: calculates Laspeyres, Paasche and Ideal price indices Lp(I), Pq(I), IDp(I) and quantity indices Lq(I), Pq(I), IDq(I) for periods I = B, . . . , N.

FNp(ref):   defines a price function $\Sigma p_i q_{ref}/\Sigma p_0 q_{ref}$

FNq(ref):   defines a quantity function $\Sigma q_i p_{ref}/\Sigma q_0 p_{ref}$

PROCprint: organizes a tabular print of price and quantity indices.

Type in Program INDICES from the following listing and RUN with the data of Table 3.5 when you are satisfied with the accuracy of your listing. You should get the indices shown in the lower half of the table.

Inspection of the output indices suggests that any one of the three composite indices tells the same story. In particular, one can see that quantity sold moved ahead up until month 8 whereas prices fluctuated up and down. The value index, numerically equal to one-hundredth of the product of IDp and IDq (unrounded values), appears to fluctuate either side of an increasing trend.

Program 3.4 INDICES:Calculates Laspeyres, Paasche and Ideal indices

```
  10 REM INDICES
  20 REM ACCEPTS PRICE & QUANTITY DATA FOR DIFFERENT PRODUCTS
  30 REM CALCULATES COMPOSITE INDEX NUMBERS
  40 DIM DATp(10,100),DATq(10,100),Lp(100)
  50 DIM Lq(100),Pp(100),Pq(100),IDp(100),IDq(100)
  60 @%=&0002000A
  70 PROCinput
  80 PROCindices
  90 PROCprint                        •
 100 END
 110
1000 DEF PROCinput
1010 PRINT "ENTER ALL DATA NUMERICALLY"
1020 INPUT "BASE PERIOD ",B
1030 INPUT "FINAL PERIOD ",N
1040 INPUT "NUMBER OF PRODUCTS ",PR
1050 FOR pr = 1 TO PR
1060 PRINT : PRINT "PRODUCT No ";pr
1070 PRINT : PRINT "PERIOD     PRICE       QUANTITY"
1080 FOR I = B TO N
1090 PRINT TAB(0);I;
1100 INPUT TAB(10) DATp(pr,I),TAB(20) DATq(pr,I)
1110 NEXT I
1120 NEXT pr
1130 ENDPROC
1140
2000 DEF PROCindices
2010 FOR I= B TO N
2020 Lp(I)=FNp(B)
2030 Pp(I)=FNp(I)
2040 IDp(I)=SQR( Lp(I)*Pp(I) )
2050 Lq(I)=FNq(B)
2060 Pq(I)=FNq(I)
2070 IDq(I)=SQR( Lq(I)*Pq(I) )
2080 NEXT I
2090 ENDPROC
2100
3000 DEF FNp(ref)
3010 NUM=0 : DENOM=0
3020 FOR pr=1 TO PR
3030 NUM=NUM + DATp(pr,I)*DATq(pr,ref)
3040 DENOM=DENOM + DATp(pr,B)*DATq(pr,ref)
3050 NEXT pr
3060 = NUM/DENOM*100
3070
4000 DEF FNq(ref)
4010 NUM=0 : DENOM=0
4020 FOR pr=1 TO PR
4030 NUM=NUM + DATq(pr,I)*DATp(pr,ref)
4040 DENOM=DENOM + DATq(pr,B)*DATp(pr,ref)
4050 NEXT pr
4060 = NUM/DENOM*100
4070
5000 DEF PROCprint
5010 PRINT : PRINT : PRINT "PRICE INDICES"
5020 PRINT "PERIOD     LASPEYRES PAASCHE   IDEAL" : PRINT
5030 FOR I= B TO N
5040 PRINT TAB(0);I;TAB(10);Lp(I);TAB(20);Pp(I);TAB(30);IDp(I)
5050 NEXT I
5060 PRINT : PRINT : PRINT "QUANTITY INDICES"
5070 PRINT "PERIOD     LASPEYRES PAASCHE   IDEAL" : PRINT
5080 FOR I= B TO N
5090 PRINT TAB(0);I;TAB(10);Lq(I);TAB(20);Pq(I);TAB(30);IDq(I)
5100 NEXT I
5110 ENDPROC
```

3.5 Index numbers in perspective

The indices described above are very simple examples of the genre. In practice there are a number of complications which have to be considered. The prime consideration must be the purpose for which an index is required, in the context of the availability and reliability of the basic data. Any summary is bound to be overtly selective in its data sources, and covertly limiting by its very summarizing nature — the scope of the index should not be so wide as to yield a meaningless series.

Problems of interpretation arise if too long a series is presented. Some products will have been phased out and new ones phased in. Technical and qualititive improvements can be made in an incremental manner over a protracted term so that like is not always compared to like, i.e. value for money is explicitly excluded from the information summary.

Problems of scale arise when there are numerous commodities. It is more convenient to construct price indices, say, from 'weighed means' of relatives (*WMR*) of individual prices where the weights W_{ref} are tied to some reference period. Such an index, WMR_i, is

$$WMR_i = \Sigma p_i/p_B \times W_{ref}/\Sigma W_{ref} \times 100$$

where the summation is taken over all the products.

When the weights W_{ref} are taken as the values v_o of expenditures in the base year (i.e. $p_o q_o$) then this index of weighted price relatives is identical to the Laspeyres price index, as the reader may confirm algebraically.

In fact, the Index of Retail Prices (RPI) is closely based on a Laspeyres quantity index. Naturally, the details of the construction of this or any other government index, such as the Index of Industrial Production, lies outside the present scope. Suffice it to say that the RPI is obtained as a weighted mean of other sub-indices, themselves defined as weighted means of relatives. The way in which the annual Family Expenditure Surveys are utilized to derive and update the weights can be somewhat complicated, and the calculations of the sub-indices are often in chain index form.

PROBLEMS

(3.1) Devise a PROCdata to read data into Program 3.1 SIMPREL from DATA statements as an alternative, which can be exercised at the user's discretion, to conversational data input in PROCinput.

(3.2) Devise a PROCedit to be called at line 65. This procedure should allow the user to alter any part of the input data.

(3.3) Modify PROCinput of SIMPREL to accept any textual identifier for the period I, such as 12/1985, in addition to the data value for period I. Modify lines 2070 and 3060 to print out the textual identifier in place of I.

(3.4) Modify DEFLATR to accept the data from the top half of Table 3.1 and to print out the real indices in the bottom half of Table 3.1 (you should introduce arrays to store sales, costs, wages, employees and deflator data).

(3.5) Modify Program INDICES to produce the additional indices as defined below, and reRUN with the data of Table 3.5:

Dribisch index $= (L + P)/2 \times 100$
Price index $= \Sigma p_i q_{ref}/\Sigma p_0 q_{ref} \times 100$
Quantity index $= \Sigma q_i p_{ref}/\Sigma q_0 p_{ref} \times 100$
Price index (Edgeworth) $= \Sigma p_i(q_0 + q_i)/\Sigma p_0(q_0 + q_i) \times 100$
Quantity index (Edgeworth) $= \Sigma q_i(p_0 + p_i)/\Sigma q_0(p_0 + p_i) \times 100$

(3.6) Write a program which forms the weighted mean of price relatives to check numerically that the index defined in Section 3.5 conforms to the Laspeyres price index when the weights W_{ref} are taken as v_0.

Chapter 4

Data fitting

Essential theory

This chapter is designed to give an introduction to data fitting.Simple linear regression on a controlled variable is first described in the context of production costs. Next, a simple logarithmic transformation of a non-linear relationship into a linear form is developed in the context of the so-called 'learning curve'. Piecewise linear regression is developed in the third section and may be omitted on a first reading. Cost-volume-profit analysis is developed for piecewise linear relationships in the final section.

4.1 A straight line fit to data

A straight line relationship is the simplest form of relationship between two quantities, such as production cost C and the production batch size N. Costs are not likely to be incurred in absolutely direct proportion to the size of a production batch, but a linear relationship may be a satisfactory approximation for some purposes.

Such approximations may be required when it is too expensive, or simply not practicable, to work out the costs of a specified batch from first principles. If a company submits priced tenders for customers on a repetitive basis, then such a costing would be based almost certainly on accumulated costing experience, rather than the detail of an individual case.

Suppose that the data in Table 4.1 below, has been derived from a close examination of the costs of producing different batch sizes of some product.

Table 4.1 Costs and batch size data

Observation	1	2	3	4	5	6	7
Batch size	12	18	24	30	36	42	48
Cost	5.27	5.68	6.25	7.21	8.02	8.71	8.42

This data has been graphed in Figure 4.1, which suggests that there may indeed be a linear relationship.

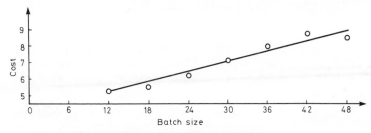

Figure 4.1 A plot of the data of Table 4.1

A search for a best linear relationship between costs and production levels makes sense only if there is a prior supposition of linearity. There are many other possibilities, and two of the major ones are considered later in this chapter. The interested reader is referred to a companion volume (*BASIC matrix methods* by J. Mason, Butterworths, 1984) for a more comprehensive treatment.

A linear relationship between costs C and batch size N may be stated as

$$C = F + V \times N$$

where F is a fixed cost

V is a constant marginal cost.

If the cost of production C_I has been established for each of several trial values of the batch size N_I then one can write

$$C_I = F + V \times N_I + e_I$$

where e_I is a residual or error term.

The problem is to establish values for the fixed cost F and the marginal (or variable) cost V per unit of production which best 'fit' the data. There are several criteria depending upon what is meant by a best fit. The simplest and perhaps the most commonly employed criterion is to fit a linear relationship to data in the 'least squares sense'; that is, a fit which minimizes the sum of the squared residuals. This is correctly described here by the term 'linear regression (of costs) upon a controlled variable (the batch size)'. Now

$$\Sigma e_I^2 = \Sigma (C_I - F - V \times N_I)^2$$

where the summation extends over the number of data pairs of C and V which are available.

Differential calculus is used to establish conditions which lead to a minimum Σe_I^2, and on equating to zero the partial derivatives with respect to V and F one finds

$$V = \frac{\Sigma(N_I - \overline{N})(C_I - \overline{C})}{\Sigma(N_I - \overline{N})^2} \quad \text{and } F = \overline{C} - V \times \overline{N}$$

where $\overline{N}$ is the average of N_I and $\overline{C}$ is the average of C_I.

A simple computer program LINEFIT for the determination of F and V is based upon a main program which calls four PROCEDURES:

PROCinput: allows the user to input the control and dependent variable values N(I) and C(I), for I = 1,2, . . . ,NN.

PROCparameters: evaluates the arithmetic means CBAR and NBAR on a first pass of the data, and the values of F and V on a second pass.

PROCprint: tabulates N(I), C(I), F + V × N(I), and residuals e_I for I = 1,2, . . . ,NN, and prints out the best fit equation together with the coefficient of determination.

PROCestimate: enables the user to make an estimate of costs $C = F + V \times N$ for any N.

Program 4.1 LINEFIT: Linear regression on a controlled variable

```
  10 REM LINEFIT
  20 REM LINEAR REGRESSION OF C ON CONTROLLED VARIABLE N
  30 DIM C(100),N(100)
  40 @%=&02040A
  50
  60 PROCinput
  70 PROCparameters
  80 PROCprint
  90 PROCestimate
 100 END
 110
1000 DEF PROCinput
1010 PRINT : INPUT "No OF DATA PAIRS ";NN
1020 PRINT "CONTROL    DEPENDENT"
1030 PRINT "VARIABLE   VARIABLE" :PRINT " N";TAB(11);"C"
1040 FOR I= 1 TO NN
1050 INPUT N(I);TAB(10);C(I)
1060 NEXT I
1070 ENDPROC
1080
2000 DEF PROCparameters
2010 SIGMAC=0 : SIGMAN=0
2020 FOR I= 1 TO NN
2030 SIGMAC=SIGMAC+C(I)
2040 SIGMAN=SIGMAN+N(I)
2050 NEXT I
2060 CBAR=SIGMAC/NN : NBAR=SIGMAN/NN
2070 NUM=0 : DENOM=0 : CD=0
2080 FOR I= 1 TO NN
2090 NUM=NUM+( N(I)-NBAR )*( C(I)-CBAR )
2100 DENOM=DENOM+( N(I)-NBAR )*( N(I)-NBAR )
2110 CD=CD+( C(I)-CBAR )*( C(I)-CBAR )
2120 NEXT I
2130 V= NUM/DENOM
2140 F =CBAR-V*NBAR
2150 CD=NUM*V/CD
2160 ENDPROC
2170
3000 DEF PROCprint
3010 PRINT : PRINT "STRAIGHT LINE OF BEST FIT  F+V*N = "
3020 PRINT F;" + ";V;" * N"
3030 PRINT : PRINT TAB(9);"N";TAB(19) "C";TAB(25) "F+V*N";
3040 PRINT TAB(32) "RESIDUAL"
3050 FOR I=1 TO NN
3060 PRINT N(I),C(I),F+V*N(I),C(I)-F-V*N(I)
3070 NEXT I
3080 PRINT : PRINT "COEFF OF DETERMINATION =";CD*100;"%"
3090 ENDPROC
3100
4000 DEF PROCestimate
4010 REPEAT
4020 PRINT
4030 INPUT "DO YOU WANT AN ESTIMATE (Y or N) ",Z$
4040 IF Z$="N" THEN ENDPROC
4050 INPUT "CONTROLLED VARIABLE VALUE = ",N
4060 C=F+V*N
4070 IF N<N(1) THEN PRINT "WARNING:CONTROL IS < DATA MIN."
4080 IF N>N(NN) THEN PRINT "WARNING:CONTROL IS > DATA MAX."
4090 PRINT "DEPENDENT  VARIABLE VALUE = ";C
4100 UNTIL FALSE
4110 ENDPROC
```

```
RUN

No OF DATA PAIRS ?7
CONTROL      DEPENDENT
VARIABLE     VARIABLE
   N            C
?12
             ?5.27
?18
             ?5.68
?24
             ?6.25
?30
             ?7.21
?36
             ?8.02
?42
             ?8.71
?48
             ?8.42

STRAIGHT LINE OF BEST FIT   F+V*N =
     3.9943 + 0.1029 * N

         N          C       F+V*N    RESIDUAL
     12.0000     5.2700     5.2286     0.0414
     18.0000     5.6800     5.8457    -0.1657
     24.0000     6.2500     6.4629    -0.2129
     30.0000     7.2100     7.0800     0.1300
     36.0000     8.0200     7.6971     0.3229
     42.0000     8.7100     8.3143     0.3957
     48.0000     8.4200     8.9314    -0.5114

COEFF OF DETERMINATION =94.5578%

DO YOU WANT AN ESTIMATE (Y or N) ?Y
CONTROLLED VARIABLE VALUE = ?10
WARNING:CONTROL IS < DATA MIN.
DEPENDENT   VARIABLE VALUE = 5.0229

DO YOU WANT AN ESTIMATE (Y or N) ?Y
CONTROLLED VARIABLE VALUE = ?54
WARNING:CONTROL IS > DATA MAX.
DEPENDENT   VARIABLE VALUE = 9.5486

DO YOU WANT AN ESTIMATE (Y or N) ?N
```

Type in LINEFIT and replicate the given RUN when you are satisfied with your listing. The output includes the residuals and it is always important to look at them very carefully. The assumption of linearity must be held with reserve, and it becomes clearly untenable when the residuals have a strongly pronounced pattern — such as large positive values for small batches and large negative values for large batches. In the present case the absolute values of the residuals tend to become numerically larger as the batch size increases, but their signs do not otherwise give rise for concern. So there is little evidence here of systematic departure from linearity.

Furthermore, the coefficient of determination is about 95 per cent, which can be interpreted as follows: some 95 per cent of the variation in the cost data has been explained on the basis of the linear relationship, which expressed to four decimal places is

Cost = 3.9943 + 0.1029 × N

95 per cent is a reassuringly high percentage. A coefficient of 100 per cent results when a line of best fit passes directly through all the data points. It would have been much smaller had the costs not varied substantially in proportion to batch size. The total 'sum of squares' $\Sigma(C_I - \overline{C})^2$ can be regarded as having an 'explained' component, and an 'unexplained' component Σe_I^2. The explained component is obtained by differencing, and the coefficient of determination is the percentage ratio of this component to the total sum of squares. This can be expressed as

$$\text{Coefficient of determination} = \frac{[\Sigma(N_I - \overline{N})\,(C_I - \overline{C})]^2}{\Sigma(N_I - \overline{N})^2\,\Sigma(C_I - \overline{C})^2} \times 100$$

The reader may have wondered why two passes of the data were employed in PROCparameters of LINEFIT. The first pass was used to evaluate the means $\overline{N}$ and $\overline{C}$ and the second to evaluate $\Sigma(N_I - \overline{N})$, $\Sigma(C_I - \overline{C})$, and $\Sigma(N_I - \overline{N})^2$ prior to substitution into the expressions for V and F. There is an alternative expression for V which entails the quantities $\Sigma N_I V_I$, ΣV_I, ΣN_I and ΣN_I^2, all of which can be evaluated on a single pass of the data. But rounding and truncation errors are more likely to occur, because the denominator of V is then determined from the difference between two large numbers $NN\Sigma N_I^2$ and $(\Sigma N_I)^2$. However, the reader is referred elsewhere (*BASIC statistics*, by J. Tennant-Smith, Butterworths, 1985) for a discussion of a better method.

Recall that the purpose was to obtain assistance in making cost estimates. This amounts to using the equation of the line of best fit with a stipulated value of the controlled variable. Notice that the output produces a warning if the value of the controlled variable lies outside the range of the original data which was used to obtain the line of best fit. This class of estimate is known as extrapolation, and it has much less reliability than an interpolated estimate, since there can be no assurance that the linear relationship holds for arbitrarily small or large volumes.

The reader should next RUN the program for the data given in Table 4.2. Here the controlled variable N is the time period and so a convenient choice is a quarterly variable with values from 1 to 14. The dependent variable C is not cost, but sales. The output is a line of best fit of the form

Sales = 211.9780 + 0.7363*N

Table 4.2   Sales for 14 quarters

	Quarter			
	1	2	3	4
1983	200	225	227	202
1984	204	228	230	207
1985	210	231	233	207
1986	209	232		

However, the coefficient of determination is only 6 per cent, which signals loud and clear that linear regression on this data is quite inappropriate. The reader should graph the data to confirm this observation. He or she should also note that the residuals have a consistent periodicity, those for quarters 1 and 4 being negative while those in quarters 2 and 3 are positive. This is fully consistent with a cyclical sales pattern over an underlying shallow trend, and this possibility must be explored in a quite different way, through time series analysis (see *BASIC forecasting*, by D. G. Johnson and M. King, Butterworths). You should do Problems 4.1 and 4.4 here.

4.2 The learning curve

Particular forms of non-linear relationships can be transformed into linear relationships. Suppose that $t = aI^b + \tau$ where t is the *average* assembly time for the first I assemblies; a and b are parameters and τ is the long run *average* time.

Taking logarithms gives

$$\log (t - \tau) = \log a + b \log I$$

This is the linear relationship

$$C = F + N \times V$$

where

$$C = \log (t - \tau) \qquad N = \log I \qquad F = \log a \qquad V = b$$

The first assembly takes the time $a + \tau$ and a negative value of b gives rise to a geometrically decreasing *average* assembly time, tending to τ in the limit. This phenomenon was first noticed in the US aircraft industry and has become known as a learning curve.

Assembly times for the first eight of a production run of aircraft components are given in Table 4.3. Figure 4.2 shows actual average assembly times t_i from the third line of Table 4.3.

Table 4.3   Assembly times for the first eight airframe components

Component i	1	2	3	4	5	6	7	8
Actual times T_i	946	593	572	589	525	555	516	549
Actual av. time t_i	946	769.5	704	675	645	630	614	606
Predicted av. time	943	773	707	669	645	628	615	606

Learning curve of best fit: $438.35 \times I^{-0.71} + 505.8$
Coefficient of determination: 99.88%

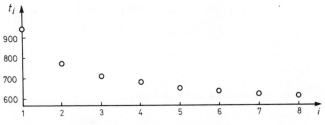

Figure 4.2 A plot of the data of Table 4.3

The method of the previous section could be used to fit a straight line in the least squares sense through the logarithmically transformed data, always provided that a value of τ was supplied. Indeed, one could repeat the process for each of a series of trial values for τ. If the 'best' value was associated with the largest coefficient of determination, then one would have a best fit equation

$$C = F + N \times V \text{ and so } a = 10^F \text{ and } b = V$$

This approach would be clearly impractical by hand calculation, but it can be carried out effectively and efficiently on a microcomputer. Program LCURVE consists of a short main program which calls the following PROCEDURES:

PROCinput: allows the user to input the observed assembly time T(I) of assemblies I = 1,2,. . . ,NN and calls FNavtime to calculate t(I), the *average* time to assemble each of the first I assemblies.

PROCiterate: calls PROCparameters (see LINEFIT) for 50 trial values of τ in the range $0 \leqslant \tau \leqslant T(NN)$, with C(I) = LOG(t(I) − τ) and N(I) = LOG(I) for I = 1,2, . . .,NN. The best value tau of TAU, the highest coefficient of determination cd, and the best values of a and b are available on completion.

PROCprint: tabulates the actual average assembly times t(I),
                  the predicted average times aI^b + tau, and the
                  residuals for I = 1,2,. . . , NN; prints the equation
                  t = aI^b + tau, together with the coefficient of
                  determination cd.
PROCestimate: allows the user to estimate the assembly time for
                  the Ith assembly.
FNavtime(i):   generates the average assembly time of the first i
                  assemblies t(i) = $1/i\Sigma T(I)$ from the actual
                  assembly times T(I) for I = 1,2,. . .,i.

Program 4.2 LCURVE: Learning curve regression

```
  10 REM LCURVE
  20 REM LEARNING CURVE REGRESSION
  30 REM LOG-LOG TRANSFORMATION ON
  40 REM AVERAGE TIME AND COMPONENT NUMBER
  50 REM REQUIRES ACTUAL TIME FOR
  60 REM COMPONENTS Nos 1 TO NN
  70 DIM C(100),T(100) ,N(100),t(100)
  80 @%=&02020A
  90
 100 PROCinput
 110 PROCiterate
 120 PROCprint
 130 PROCestimate
 140 END
 150
1000 DEF PROCinput
1010 INPUT "MAX No COMPONENTS";NN
1020 PRINT
1030 PRINT "COMPONENT ACTUAL"
1040 PRINT "NUMBER      TIME"
1050 FOR I= 1 TO NN
1060 PRINT TAB(4);I;TAB(14);:INPUT T(I)
1070 t(I)=FNavtime(I)
1080 NEXT I
1090 ENDPROC
1100
2000 DEF PROCparameters
2010 SIGMAC=0 : SIGMAN=0
2020 FOR I= 1 TO NN
2030 SIGMAC=SIGMAC+C(I)
2040 SIGMAN=SIGMAN+N(I)
2050 NEXT I
2060 CBAR=SIGMAC/NN : NBAR=SIGMAN/NN
2070 NUM=0 : DENOM=0 : CD=0
2080 FOR I= 1 TO NN
2090 NUM=NUM+( N(I)-NBAR )*( C(I)-CBAR )
2100 DENOM=DENOM+( N(I)-NBAR )*( N(I)-NBAR )
2110 CD=CD+( C(I)-CBAR )*( C(I)-CBAR )
2120 NEXT I
2130 V= NUM/DENOM
2140 F =CBAR-V*NBAR
2150 CD=NUM*V/CD
2160 ENDPROC
2170
```

```
3000 DEF PROCiterate
3010 cd=0
3020 S=T(NN)/50
3030 FOR TAU=0 TO T(NN) STEP S
3040 FOR I= 1 TO NN
3050 C(I)=LOG( t(I)-TAU ) :N(I)=LOG(I)
3060 NEXT I
3070 PROCparameters
3080 IF CD>cd THEN cd=CD :tau=TAU : a=10^F : b=V
3090 NEXT TAU
3100 ENDPROC
3110
4000 DEF PROCprint
4010 PRINT
4020 PRINT " COMPONENT    AVERAGE   ESTIMATED RESIDUAL"
4030 PRINT "   NUMBER      TIME        TIME"
4040 FOR I= 1 TO NN
4050 PRINT I,t(I),a*I^b+tau,t(I)-a*I^b-tau
4060 NEXT I
4070 PRINT :PRINT "COEFF OF DETERMINATION ";cd*100
4080 PRINT : PRINT "BEST FIT LEARNING CURVE "
4090 PRINT a;"*I^";TAB(14) b;TAB(22)"+";TAB(24) tau
4100 ENDPROC
4110
5000 DEF PROCestimate
5010 REPEAT
5020 INPUT "DO YOU WANT AN ASSEMBLY TIME ESTIMATE (Y/N) ",Z$
5030 IF Z$="N" THEN ENDPROC
5040 INPUT "INPUT AN ASSEMBLY NUMBER >1 ",I
5050 t=a*( I^(b+1)-(I-1)^(b+1) )+tau
5060 PRINT "ACTUAL ASSEMBLY TIME PREDICTION IS ";t
5070 UNTIL FALSE
5080 ENDPROC
5090
6000 DEF FNavtime(i)
6010 TC=0
6020 FOR j= 1 TO i
6030 TC=TC+T(j)
6040 NEXT j
6050 =TC/i

 RUN
MAX No COMPONENTS?8

COMPONENT ACTUAL
NUMBER      TIME
   1.00      ?946
   2.00      ?593
   3.00      ?572
   4.00      ?589
   5.00      ?525
   6.00      ?555
   7.00      ?516
   8.00      ?549

 COMPONENT   AVERAGE   ESTIMATED RESIDUAL
   NUMBER      TIME        TIME
   1.00      946.00     943.43      2.57
   2.00      769.50     773.50     -4.00
   3.00      703.67     706.55     -2.88
   4.00      675.00     669.44      5.56
   5.00      645.00     645.44     -0.44
   6.00      630.00     628.45      1.55
   7.00      613.71     615.70     -1.98
   8.00      605.62     605.73     -0.10

COEFF OF DETERMINATION 99.88

BEST FIT LEARNING CURVE
     438.35*I^ -0.71   + 505.08
DO YOU WANT AN ASSEMBLY TIME ESTIMATE (Y/N) ?Y
INPUT AN ASSEMBLY NUMBER >1 ?20
ACTUAL ASSEMBLY TIME PREDICTION IS 520.75
DO YOU WANT AN ASSEMBLY TIME ESTIMATE (Y/N) ?N
```

Type in LCURVE from the listing above (first load LINEFIT and DELETE 10,1080, and DELETE 3000,4110 to avoid the tedium of entering PROCparameters) and RUN with the data of the first two rows of Table 4.3 (the machine may require a minute or so to carry out the 50 regressions). Your output should agree with the rest of the table, and a prediction for the assembly time of the twentieth airframe is 521.

Such models can be applied to a wide variety of circumstances, such as plant maintenance costs which decrease with experience, or the costs associated with obtaining repeat orders. However, caution should be exercised when using the model for extrapolation beyond the immediate future: it is a useful model for short-term decision making, such as budgeting, but it is doubtful whether it is sensible to employ it for medium or long term forecasts. Methods for the determination of confidence limits are omitted here.

You should do Problems 4.5 and 4.6 at this juncture.

*4.3 Fitting a piecewise linear function by least squares

A linear relationship (or a transformation of a linear relationship) may be quite inadequate for fitting the data to hand. Thus a RUN of LINEFIT on the data of Table 4.4 yields a very low coefficient of determination of 36%.

Table 4.4   Further cost and batch size data

Observation	1	2	3	4	5	6	7	8	9	10
Batch size	10	20	30	40	50	60	70	80	90	100
Cost	220	252	273	281	298	211	240	273	299	403

This data is graphed in Figure 4.3, showing that the costs increase more or less linearly up to mid-range batch sizes: Then there is a sudden decrease in costs followed by a second and continuing rise. This pattern of costs could be due to a change in technology, which only becomes feasible in the light of opportunity costs for production of the larger batches. The costs for new technology production once again advance with batch size in a more or less linear fashion.

Although it is obviously possible in this simple example to RUN LINEFIT twice, for lower and higher levels of output, this would be tiresome with a large number of linear segments. The practical utility of piecewise linear data fitting should be self-evident, as the next section on cost-volume-profit analysis will convincingly demonstrate in one particular case. The L linear segments are said

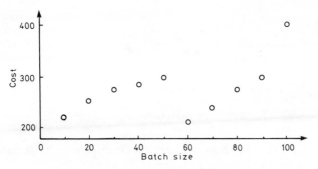

Figure 4.3 A piecewise linear function: data from Table 4.4

to join at 'knots' $n_1, n_2, \ldots, n_{L-1}$. Thus one can relate the cost C to output N by a piecewise linear function which includes a fixed cost element f, and marginal costs v_i for outputs in the range $n_{i-1} < N \leqslant n_i$ as follows:

$$C = f + n_1(v_1 - v_2) + n_2(v_2 - v_3) + \ldots + n_{i-1}(v_{i-1} - v_i) + N v_i$$

or

$$C = c_0 + c_1(N - n_0) + c_2(N - n_1) + \ldots + c_i(N - n_{i-1})$$
where $n_0 = 0$

These alternatives are shown in Figure 4.4 for the case of a 2-piece linear relationship (i.e. $L = 2$).

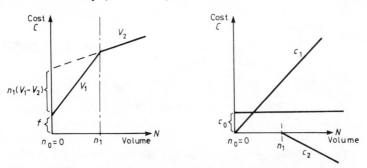

Figure 4.4 Two alternative formulations of 2-piece linearity

The correspondence between the two alternatives is given by

$$f = c_0 \qquad\qquad c_0 = f$$
$$v_j = \sum_{k=1}^{j} c_k \qquad\qquad c_j = v_j - v_{j-1}$$

or

Now the second formulation can be written even more compactly as

$$C = c_0 + \sum_j c_j(N - n_{j-1})_+$$

where

$$(N - n_{j-1})_+ = N - n_{j-1} \text{ if } > 0$$
$$= 0 \text{ otherwise}$$

It is now convenient to use this equation to express the sum of squared residuals, S.S., as follows:

$$\text{S.S.} = \sum_{I=1}^{NN} [c_0 + \sum_j^L c_j(N_I - n_{j-1})_+ - C_I]^2$$

where the first summation extends over the NN observations.

On equating to zero the partial derivatives of S.S. with respect to $c_0, c_1, c_2, \ldots, c_L$ one finds the following $L + 1$ linear equations in $c_0, c_1, c_2, \ldots, c_L$:

$$\sum_{I=1}^{NN} \{c_0 + \sum_{j=1}^L c_j(N_I - n_{j-1})_+\} = \sum_{I=1}^{NN} C_I$$

$$\sum_{I=1}^{NN} \{[c_0 + \sum_{j=1}^L c_j(N_I - n_{j-1})_+](N_I - n_{j-1})_+\} = \sum_{I=1}^{NN} C_I(N_I - n_{i-1})_+$$

for $i = 1, 2, \ldots, L$.

Written in matrix form, these equations become A $\underline{c} = \underline{b}$ where $\underline{c} = (c_0, c_1, c_2, \ldots, c_L)$ and $|b_i| = \Sigma C_I(N_I - n_{i-1})_+$

$$|a_{oo}| = NN \qquad |a_{oj}| = |a_{jo}| = \Sigma(N_I - n_{j-1})_+$$

$$|a_{ij}| = |a_{ji}| = \Sigma[(N_I - n_{i-1})_+ (N_I - n_{j-1})_+]$$

for $i = 1, 2, \ldots, L$
$\quad j = 1, 2, \ldots, L$.

Thus A is symmetric and this fact allows the use of a simplified method of solution (Gaussian elimination for a symmetric matrix of coefficients). The equations are linearly independent if there is at least one data point for each segment l for $l = 2, 3, \ldots, L$ and at least two data points for the initial segment. The equations could well be ill-conditioned, however, with a likelihood that increases with increasing L. These equations can be seen to reduce to the familiar equations for simple linear regression when $L = 1$ upon substitution for the c_i.

A structured program PIECELN has a short main program which calls the following procedures:

PROCinput: allows the user to input the observations $C(I)$ and $N(I)$ for $I = 1, 2, \ldots , NN$, and the ordinates of knots n_i for $i = 1, 2, \ldots , L$.

PROCmatrix: generates the elements of A and $\underline{b}$.

PROCgauss: solves for $\underline{c}$ by a standard Gaussian elimination (after Program 5.5 from *BASIC matrix methods*, by J. Mason, Butterworths, 1984).

PROCtransform: finds f and $v(i)$ for $i = 1, 2, \ldots , L$.

PROCprint: prints out the best L-piece linear relationship in the least squared sense: also prints the residuals and the coefficient of determination.

FNC(X): returns the value of the dependent variable C for a value of the controlled variable X.

A listing of Program PIECELN is given below. The program is rudimentary and no particular efforts have been made to avoid truncation or rounding errors, or to recognize the possible existence of ill-conditioning. A RUN with the data of Table 4.4 follows the listing. For the (subjective) choice of knots as shown, the coefficient of determination is a modest 91 per cent.

Program 4.3 PIECELN: Piecewise linear regression

```
10 REM PIECELN
20 REM PIECEWISE LINEAR REGRESSION
30 REM FOR DETAILS OF PROCgauss REFER BASIC matrix methods
40 REM BY J.MASON,BUTTERWORTHS 1984
50 DIM C(100),N(100),n(10),A(11,11),B(11),c(11),v(11)
60 @%=&02040A
70
80 PROCinput
90 PROCmatrix
100 PROCgauss
110 PROCtransform
120 PROCprint
130 END
140
1000 DEF PROCinput
1010 CBAR=0 : PRINT : INPUT "No DATA PAIRS ";NN
1020 PRINT "CONTROL    DEPENDENT"
1030 PRINT "VARIABLE    VARIABLE" :PRINT " N";TAB(11);"C"
1040 FOR I= 1 TO NN
1050 INPUT N(I);TAB(10);C(I) : CBAR=CBAR+C(I)
1060 NEXT I : CBAR=CBAR/NN
1070 PRINT:INPUT "No OF LINE SEGS. ";L
1080 PRINT : IF L>1 THEN PRINT "KNOT   ORDINATE"
1090 l=1
1100 REPEAT
1110 IF l<L THEN PRINT STR$(l) TAB(10) ; : INPUT n(l)
1120 l = l+1
1130 UNTIL l>=L
1140 ENDPROC
1150
2000 DEF PROCmatrix
2010 A(0,0)=NN
2020 FOR I= 1 TO NN
2030 B(0)=B(0)+C(I)
2040 NEXT I
2050 FOR j= 1 TO L
2060 FOR I= 1 TO NN
2070 TERM=N(I)-n(j-1)
2080 IF TERM <0 THEN TERM =0
2090 A(0,j)=A(0,j)+TERM
2100 NEXT I
2110 A(j,0)=A(0,j)
2120 NEXT j
2130 FOR i = 1 TO L
2140 FOR I= 1 TO NN
2150 PROD=N(I)-n(i-1)
2160 IF PROD <0 THEN PROD=0
2170 B(i)=B(i)+PROD*C(I)
2180 NEXT I
2190 FOR j= 1 TO L
2200 FOR I= 1 TO NN
2210 PROD =N(I)-n(j-1) : IF PROD<0 THEN PROD=0
2220 PROD=PROD*(N(I)-n(i-1)) : IF PROD<0 THEN PROD=0
2230 A(i,j)=A(i,j)+PROD
2240 NEXT I
2250 NEXT j
2260 NEXT i
2270 ENDPROC
2280
```

```
3000 DEF PROCgauss
3010 FOR K=0 TO L-1
3020 FOR I=K+1 TO L
3030 M=-A(K,I)/A(K,K)
3040 FOR J= I TO L
3050 A(I,J)=A(I,J)+M*A(K,J)
3060 NEXT J
3070 B(I)=B(I)+M*B(K)
3080 NEXT I
3090 NEXT K
3100 c(L)=B(L)/A(L,L)
3110 FOR I=L-1 TO 0 STEP -1
3120 D=B(I)
3130 FOR J=I+1 TO L
3140 D=D-c(J)*A(I,J)
3150 NEXT J
3160 c(I)=D/A(I,I)
3170 NEXT I
3180
4000 DEF PROCtransform
4010 f=c(0)
4020 v(1)=c(1)
4030 FOR l = 2 TO L
4040 v(l)=v(l-1)+c(l)
4050 NEXT l
4060 ENDPROC
4070
5000 DEF PROCprint
5010 PRINT : SS=0 : T=0 : PRINT "PIECEWISE LINEAR FIT = "
5020 PRINT c(0)
5030 FOR l= 1 TO L
5040 PRINT "+ (N-";n(l-1);")+ *";c(l)
5050 NEXT l
5060 PRINT : PRINT "OR ALTERNATIVELY"
5070 PRINT "FIXED ELEMENT =";f :PRINT "MARG. RATE     <=KNOT"
5080 FOR l=1 TO L
5090 PRINT v(l),n(l)
5100 NEXT l
5110 PRINT : PRINT TAB(9);"N           C      FITTED    RESIDUAL"
5120 FOR I= 1 TO NN
5130 PRINT N(I),C(I),FNC(N(I)),C(I)-FNC(N(I))
5140 SS=SS+(C(I)-FNC(N(I)))^2 : T=T+(CBAR-C(I))^2
5150 NEXT I
5160 CD=(T-SS)/T*100
5170 PRINT : PRINT "COEFF OF DETERMINATION =";CD
5180 ENDPROC
5190
6000 DEF FNC(X)
6010 TERM=0 : C=c(0)
6020 FOR l= 1 TO L
6030 TERM=X-n(l-1)
6040 IF TERM<0 THEN TERM=0
6050 C=C+TERM*c(l)
6060 NEXT l
6070 =C
```

```
RUN

No DATA PAIRS ?10
CONTROL    DEPENDENT
VARIABLE   VARIABLE
  N          C
?10
            ?220
?20
            ?252
?30
            ?273
?40
            ?281
?50
            ?298
?60
            ?211
?70
            ?240
?80
            ?273
?90
            ?299
?100
            ?403

No OF LINE SEGS. ?3

KNOT   ORDINATE
 1        ?50
 2        ?60

PIECEWISE LINEAR FIT =
  209.3000
+ (N-0.0000)+ *1.8500
+ (N-50.0000)+ *-12.3700
+ (N-60.0000)+ *14.9500

OR ALTERNATIVELY
FIXED ELEMENT =209.3000
MARG. RATE    <=KNOT
    1.8500   50.0000
  -10.5200   60.0000
    4.4300    0.0000

         N          C      FITTED   RESIDUAL
   10.0000   220.0000   227.8000    -7.8000
   20.0000   252.0000   246.3000     5.7000
   30.0000   273.0000   264.8000     8.2000
   40.0000   281.0000   283.3000    -2.3000
   50.0000   298.0000   301.8000    -3.8000
   60.0000   211.0000   196.6000    14.4000
   70.0000   240.0000   240.9000    -0.9000
   80.0000   273.0000   285.2000   -12.2000
   90.0000   299.0000   329.5000   -30.5000
  100.0000   403.0000   373.8000    29.2000

COEFF OF DETERMINATION =91.2140
```

PIECELN requires the user to input the number of linear segments L. It would obviously be advisable to start any attempt at data fitting with the simplest case of a linear fit, and the reader may care to confirm that a RUN on the data from Table 4.1 with L = 1 does indeed reproduce the best linear fit. A similar run with the data of Table 4.4 returns a coefficient of determination of 36 per cent, and a further RUN with L = 5 and knots at 30, 55, 56 and 95, say, naturally returns an excellent fit of 99.82 per cent. Presumably one would use the minimum L consistent with achieving a desired degree of fit. PIECELN also requires the user to select the ordinates of the knot, and it may be far from obvious precisely what the best values should be.

RUN the program on the data from Table 4.4 with knots at 49 and 61. You should find a fit with a coefficient of determination of 92.6 per cent. The reader may have wondered throughout this section whether it is reasonable to ignore the likelihood of a dramatic discontinuity in mid-range in the data of Table 4.4, and much depends on the detailed circumstances. The purpose here has been to use as simple an example as possible to demonstrate the main analytical points. The reader may care to repeat the task of fitting a piecewise linear function to the data of Table 4.4 on the supposition of an abrupt change in manufacturing technology once 55 or more units are produced. Now do Problem* 4.7.

4.4 Cost-volume-profit (CVP) analysis

The general objective in cost-volume-profit (CVP) analysis is to identify the level of commercial activity which maximizes the contribution to profits in absolute terms, i.e. maximizes the revenue less the operating costs. Both costs and revenue functions are assumed to be piecewise linear functions.

Piecewise linear functions can arise quite naturally. The piecewise linear production cost C in the following numerical example arises from the aggregation of linear energy costs C^E, and piecewise linear labour costs C^L, machining costs C^M and raw material costs C^R.

The energy cost C^E is a directly variable cost. The labour cost C^L results from an initial training and familiarization cost, and a marginal cost rate which increases once overtime working becomes necessary to produce large batches. The machining cost C^M consists of a constant marginal cost per unit of output plus periodic set-up costs incurred every so many units. The first unit produced after a second (or subsequent) set-up has a marginal cost given by the sum of the set-up cost plus the machining cost *per se*.

A bulk discount applies to the variable raw material costs C^R beyond a threshold delivery volume, and there is a fixed delivery cost. The marginal cost of the first unit at the threshold volume could be negative as in case 1 of Figure 4.5: this occurs if the saving which follows the introduction of the discount to the whole delivery is numerically larger than the discounted marginal cost.

Case 2 of Figure 4.5 would apply if the threshold volume were ordered wherever the actual raw material requirements lay between this volume and the break-even volume: there is then a zero marginal cost in this volume range. It is assumed that the second case applies here.

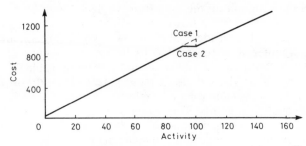

Figure 4.5 Two cases for piecewise linear raw material costs C^R

A piecewise linear cost-volume relationship is shown in Figure 4.6. Here we find three linear segments, with gradients V_1, V_2, V_3 and knots at n_1 and n_2.

The cost C of N units of activity is then

$$
\begin{aligned}
C = F + V_1N & \qquad \text{for} \qquad N \leq n_1 \\
F + V_1 N_1 + V_2(N - N_1) & \qquad n_1 < N \leq n_2 \\
F + V_1 N_1 + V_2(N_2 - N_1) + V_3(N - N_2) & \qquad n_2 < N
\end{aligned}
$$

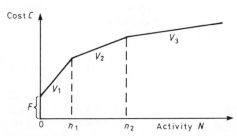

Figure 4.6 A piecewise linear cost-volume relationship

Table 4.5 summarizes the numerical values for parameters F, V and N of the piecewise linear costs for the numerical example and also gives the marginal rates of revenue r.

The parameters for the production costs C are obtained from the following:

$$f = F^E + F^L + F^M + F^R \text{ and } v = V^E + V^L + V^M + V^R.$$

Table 4.5   Piecewise linear parameters

Element	Fixed cost	Marginal rates for	$N< =$ knots
Energy C^E	$F^E = 0$	$V_1^E = 12$	150
Labour C^L	$F^L = 50$	$V_1^L = 8$	120
		$= 10$	150
Machining C^M	$F^M = 20$	$V_1^M = 7$	90
		$= 27$	91
		$= 7$	150
Raw Materials C^R	$F^R = 8$	$V_1^R = 10$	90
		$= 0$	100
		$= 9$	150
Revenue	—	$r_1 = 45$	90
		$r_2 = 37$	150

It is clear that the marginal costs V have to be selected from the appropriate range of activity levels. These aggregate production cost parameters are given in Table 4.6 (the convention is that lower case symbols are employed for aggregate cost parameters).

Table 4.6   Parameters for aggregate production cost: data from Table 4.5

Fixed cost	Marginal rate for	$N<=$ knots
$f = 78$	$v_1 = 37$	90
	$v_2 = 47$	91
	$v_3 = 27$	100
	$v_4 = 36$	120
	$v_5 = 38$	150

It is not immediately obvious how one could accomplish this sorting process in an effective and efficient manner on a large scale. But the aggregation of cost parameters can be achieved in stages. We could first choose to aggregate the parameters for the energy costs $\{C^E\}$ with those of the labour costs C^L. The resulting parameters for $\{C^E + C^L\}$ could be aggregated to those of the machining costs C^M. Finally, the parameters for $\{C^E + C^L + C^M\}$ could be aggregated to those of the raw materials costs C^R. The first four stages in Table 4.7 illustrate this sequence for the numerical data of Table 4.5.

It is easy to extend this algorithmic approach to the case of profitability analysis. The marginal profit rate p is given by $p = r + (-c)$ where the marginal parameters have to be selected

Table 4.7   Sequential aggregation for stages 1 to 5

	Element of cost or revenue			aggregate	fixed	marginal	knots
Stage	Fixed	Marginal rates	Knots	category		rates	
1	$F^L = 50$	$V_1^L = 8$	120	$\{C^E\}$	$f=0$	$v_1 = 12$	150
		$V_2^L = 10$	150				
2	$F^M = 20$	$V_1^M = 7$	90	$\{C^E + C^L\}$	$f=50$	$v_1 = 2$	120
		$V_2^M = 27$	91			$v_2 = 22$	150
		$V_3^M = 7$	150				
3	$F^R = 8$	$V_1^R = 10$	90	$\{C^E+C^L+C^M\}$	$f=70$	$v_1 = 27$	90
		$V_2^R = 0$	100			$v_2 = 47$	91
		$V_3^R = 9$	150			$v_3 = 27$	120
						$v_4 = 29$	150
4		$r_1 = 45$	90	$-\{C^E+C^L+C^M+C^R\}$	$f=-78$	$v_1 = -37$	90
		$r_2 = 37$	150			$v_2 = -47$	91
						$v_3 = -27$	100
						$v_4 = -36$	120
						$v_5 = -38$	150
5				PROFIT	$f=-78$	$v_1 = 8$	90
						$v_2 = -10$	91
						$v_3 = 10$	100
						$v_4 = 1$	120
						$v_5 = -1$	150

from the appropriate range of activity levels. Consequently we take the parameters for the aggregate costs, and reverse the sign of the marginal and fixed cost parameters prior to the final stage of aggregation.

This final aggregation results in the profit parameters at the foot of Table 4.7, from which Figure 4.7 has been constructed. Contribution to profits are maximized at an activity level of 120. It is evident from the algorithmic basis of the whole approach that the profitability relationship is piecewise linear if the cost and revenue relationships are likewise piecewise linear.

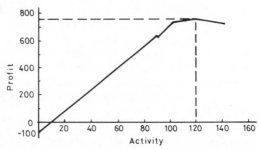

Figure 4.7 A piecewise linear profit-volume relationship

A formal algorithm follows for merging the Ith line, say, from the left side of Table 4.7 into the list on the right side, after line $i-1$.

Step 1. If $n_{i-1} < N_I < n_i$ then introduce an extra line into the right-hand list after line $i-1$ with a knot at N_I.

Step 2. Add V_I to $v_j, v_j + 1, \ldots, v_i$ in lines j to i respectively where $n_{j-1} = N_{I-1}$.

A computer program can carry out these recursive calculations very quickly. A short main program dimensions a marginal parameter array v, and a knot array n, which jointly define a piecewise linear function with up to 100 linear segments (easily increased if required). The main program calls the following PROCEDURES.

PROCinput_costs: enables the user to input the fixed, and marginal cost parameters and the knots for an arbitrarily large number of cost elements EMAX ($= 4$ in the above example). PROCstep2 is called after each INPUT of a complete set of cost data for the next stage in the aggregation of parameters.

PROCinput_revenue: reverses the signs of the aggregate cost parameters and allows the user to input the marginal revenue data.

PROCstep2:   calls PROCstep1 if necessary, and subsequently carries out step 2 of the algorithm.

PROCstep1:   carries out step 1 of the algorithm.

PROCprint_table: prints out aggregate fixed, marginal and total costs and revenues.

Type in Program CVP from the listing and RUN with the data of Table 4.5. The output is easy to assimilate and is seen to conform to earlier results. The program requires very little memory and executes extremely quickly.

Program 4.4 CVP: Cost-volume-profit analysis.

```
  10 REM CVP
  20 REM COST VOLME PROFIT ANALYSIS FOR PIECEWISE LINEAR FNS.
  30 DIM v(100),n(100)
  40
  50 PROCinput_costs
  60 PROCprint_table
  70 PROCinput_revenue
  80 PROCprint_table
  90 END
 100
1000 DEFPROCinput_costs
1010 INPUT "MAXIMUM VOLUME ",NN
1020 INPUT "MAX NO OF COST ELEMENTS",EMAX   :Z$="C"
1030 REPEAT
1040 E=E+1
1050 PRINT "COST ELEMENT ";E
1060 INPUT "NO OF LINEAR SEGMENTS ",L
1070 INPUT "FIXED COST ",F
1080 PRINT "MARG.      KNOTS"
1090 PRINT "COST"
1100 PRINT "V","N"
1110 FOR I=1 TO L
1120 INPUT V
1130 IF I<L INPUT TAB(10),N ELSE N=NN
1140 IF E=1 THEN v(I)=V:n(I)=N
1150 IF E>1 THEN PROCstep2
1160 NEXT I
1170 IF E=1 THEN l=L : f=F
1180 UNTIL E=EMAX
1190 PRINT
1200 ENDPROC
1210
2000 DEF PROCstep2
2010 IF I=1 THEN f=f+F : j=1
2020 n(0)=0
2030 i=0
2050 REPEAT
2060 i=i+1
2070 UNTIL N>=n(i-1)+1 AND N<=n(i)
2080 IF N<n(i) THEN PROCstepl
2090 REPEAT
2100 v(j)=v(j)+V
2110 j=j+1
2120 UNTIL j=i+1
2130 ENDPROC
2140
3000 DEF PROCstepl
3010 FOR k=l+1 TO i+1 STEP -1
3020 v(k)=v(k-1)
3030 n(k)=n(k-1)
3040 NEXT k
3050 n(i)=N
3060 l=l+1
3070 ENDPROC
3080
4000 DEF PROCprint_table
4010 IF Z$="C" PRINT "COST-VOLUME PARAMETER TABLE"
4020 IF Z$="P" PRINT "PROFITABILITY-VOLUME PARAMETER TABLE"
4030 PRINT : PRINT "FIXED COMPONENT ";f : PRINT
4040 PRINT TAB(2) "SEGMENT    MARGINAL      KNOT     TOTAL"
4050 PRINT TAB(14);:IF Z$="C" PRINT "  COST" TAB(35) "COST"
4060 IF Z$="P" PRINT "PROFIT" TAB(33) "PROFIT"
4070 c = f : PRINT
4080 FOR i=1 TO l
4090 c = c + v(i)*( n(i)-n(i-1) )
4100 PRINT i , v(i) , n(i) , c
4110 NEXT i
4120 PRINT
4130 ENDPROC
4140
```

```
6000 DEF PROCinput_revenue
6010 PRINT "ENTER REVENUE DATA" :Z$="P"
6020 FOR i=1 TO 1
6030 v(i)=-v(i)
6040 NEXT i
6050 f=-f
6060 INPUT "No OF LINEAR SEGMENTS ",L
6070 F=0
6080 PRINT "MARG.     KNOTS"
6090 PRINT "REVENUE"
6100 PRINT "S","N"
6110 FOR I= 1 TO L
6120 INPUT V
6130 IF I<L INPUT TAB(10),N ELSE N=NN
6140 PROCstep2
6150 NEXT I
6160 PRINT
6170 ENDPROC


  RUN
MAXIMUM VOLUME ?150
MAX NO OF COST ELEMENTS?4
COST ELEMENT 1
NO OF LINEAR SEGMENTS ?1
FIXED COST ?0
MARG.     KNOTS
COST
V         N
?12
COST ELEMENT 2
NO OF LINEAR SEGMENTS ?2
FIXED COST ?50
MARG.     KNOTS
COST
V         N
?8
          ?120
?10
COST ELEMENT 3
NO OF LINEAR SEGMENTS ?3
FIXED COST ?20
MARG.     KNOTS
COST
V         N
?7
          ?90
?27
          ?91
?7
COST ELEMENT 4
NO OF LINEAR SEGMENTS ?3
FIXED COST ?8
MARG.     KNOTS
COST
V         N
?10
          ?90
?0
          ?100
?9

COST-VOLUME PARAMETER TABLE

FIXED COMPONENT 78
```

SEGMENT	MARGINAL COST	KNOT	TOTAL COST
1	37	90	3408
2	47	91	3455
3	27	100	3698
4	36	120	4418
5	38	150	5558

```
ENTER REVENUE DATA
No OF LINEAR SEGMENTS ?2
MARG.      KNOTS
REVENUE
S          N
?45
           ?90
?37
```

```
PROFITABILITY-VOLUME  PARAMETER  TABLE
```

```
FIXED COMPONENT -78
```

SEGMENT	MARGINAL PROFIT	KNOT	TOTAL PROFIT
1	8	90	642
2	-10	91	632
3	10	100	722
4	1	120	742
5	-1	150	712

Problems

(4.1) Amend LINEFIT to include a PROCread_data which reads from DATA statements as an alternative to conversational data input in PROCinput:

```
50 INPUT "ENTER Y FOR CONVERSATIONAL INPUT, N FOR DATA READ", Q$
60 IF Q$ = "Y" THEN PROCinput ELSE PROCread_data
```

You should devise PROCread_data to read NN, and then $N(I)$ and $C(I)$ for $I = 1, 2, \ldots , NN$ from DATA statements starting at line 9500. PROCread_data should then call PROCdata_print which should tabulate $N(I)$ and $C(I)$ prior to returning to the main program.

(4.2) Amend LINEFIT to include a PROCedit which allows the user to edit the data:

```
65 INPUT "ENTER E FOR EDIT OPTION", E$
66 IF E$ = "E" THEN PROCedit
```

You should devise PROCedit so that the user can conveniently edit any item(s) of data.

(4.3) There are occasions when the value of F is known in advance, the so-called 'forced intercept' case. This gives rise to the following expression for V which minimizes the sum of squared residuals:

$$V = \frac{\Sigma(C_I - F)N_I}{\Sigma N_I^2}$$

This result is contained in standard works on regression theory. Amend PROCparameters of LINEFIT to work in this way, and reRUN using F = 4 and the data of Table 4.1. PROCinput should allow the user to specify F. Note that the concept of a coefficient of determination is not valid here, since a very poor choice of F could easily lead to a sum of squared residuals in excess of $\Sigma(C_I - \overline{C})^2$. So make the following amendments to PROCprint.

```
3005 SS = 0
3065 SS = SS + ( C(I) - F - V*N(I) )^2
3080 PRINT : PRINT "R.M.S. ERROR = "; SQR(SS/NN)
```

(4.4) Develop the program from Problem 4.3 to allow the user to input a value for a false origin N0 for the controlled variable N. Then make the changes

```
1055 N(I) = N(I) - N0
3020 PRINT F; " + ";V;" *(N-N0)"
3060 PRINT N(I) + N0, C(I), F+V*N(I), C(I)-F-V*N(I)
4055 N = N=N0
```

A RUN with F = 8.9314 and N0 = 48 and six data pairs (i.e. exclude the case N = 48) will force the regression through the point 48, 9.9314 and the results should therefore tally exactly with the RUN of LINEFIT in the text.

(4.5) The non-linear relationship $y = a*b^x$ can be transformed into a linear relationship between the log y and variable x.

analogous to log $y = $ log a + log $b * x$
$$C = F + V * N$$

Modify the program from Problem 4.4 to take the LOG(C(I)) and LOG(F) in the lines following their INPUTs.

Write b = (1 + R/100) where R is an average percentage rate given by R = 100*(b − 1) or R = 100*(10^V − 1). Print out R and amend line 4090 to print 10^c. Now use this program to find an average annual rate of inflation R% and to estimate the RPI for 1985 and 1986 from the following data.

Year	1976	1977	1978	1979	1980	1981	1982	1983	1984
RPI	157.1	182.0	197.1	223.5	263.5	295.0	320.4	335.1	351.8

(Average annual index values from table 18.3, Monthly Digest of Statistics, HMSO.)

Force an intercept of 351.8 in 1984 and RUN with the data from preceding years, and then RUN with 1980 to 1983 data. What qualifications attach to these forecasts? (The actual average RPI was 373.2 in 1985.)

(4.6) The works accountant needs to budget for maintenance costs on chemical plant for the coming year. Plant is shut down for maintenance every three months, and the following costs were incurred last year:

Quarter	1	2	3	4
Shut-down cost (£'000)	8.0	6.4	6.0	5.6

Modify LCURVE to print-out the 'rate of learning' 2^{-b} and the sum of predicted costs for quarters 5 to 8. What qualifying observations attach to this forecast?

*(4.7) Develop PIECELN to allow the user to select provisional knot ordinates, and then, for each knot in turn, to specify a number of trial evaluations for knot ordinates over a stated range. A knot must be contained within the range given by its adjacent knots and there must be at least one data point between each knot. Find the best fitting lines with L = 1, 2, 3, 4, 5 for the data of Table 4.4.

*(4.8) A particular product has the following price structure:

Quantity ordered	q	1–99	100–249	250–499	500–999	1000+
Unit price	$p(q)$	10.20	9.95	9.65	9.30	8.80

The total annual cost of stockholding C is the sum of the annual purchase costs and the interest costs on the capital tied up in stocks. If the rate of interest is $I\%$ per annum, and the average weekly demand is for 10 stock items then it can be shown that

$$C = 520 \, p(q) + 0.5 \, q \, I \, p(q)$$

Use CVP to derive the piecewise linear cost function C, and show that the optimum stock policy is to order 250 items when $I = 20\%$ at an annual cost of £5066.

*(4.9) Develop CVP to identify the optimum solution automatically for Problem 4.8, and to step through the values of I from 8% to 26%. Use the results to plot the optimum batch size against I.

*(4.10) A particular product has the following piecewise linear revenue-volume relationship, and incremental fixed costs. Show, using CVP, that the optimum output is 8000 units if all of it can be sold.

Quantity sold	<=1000	<=4000	<=9000	<=11000	<=15000
Unit revenue £	1.75	2.00	2.30	1.80	0.50
Incremental fixed costs	5000 at 0 units		8000 at 8000 units		

*(4.11) In addition to the product from Problem 4.10 the company can produce a second with the following piecewise linear parameters:

Quantity sold	$\leq=6000$	$\leq=11000$	$\leq=18000$
Unit revenue £	2.25	2.0	1.0
Inc. fixed costs £	4000 at 0 units	5000 at 10000 units	

If each unit takes 0.5 machine hours and 0.42 machine hours for products one and two respectively, find the optimum product mix if machine time is limited to 10000 hours.

Hint: Transform the volume parameters to the machine-time domain and RUN CVP for each product individually. Graph the profit-time relationship for each product on the same graph. Work towards the constrained optimum from the unconstrained optimum being guided by the marginal profit rates.

*(4.12) Restructure step 2 of the algorithm for cost-volume-profit analysis to work on the basis of the following formulation of piecewise linearity (from Section 4.3):

$$C = c_0 + \sum_j c_j (N - n_{j-1})_+ \text{ where } (N - n_{j-1})_+ = N - n_{j-1} \text{ if } > 0$$
$$= 0 \text{ otherwise}$$

Amend CVP to work on this basis.

Chapter 5

Critical path network analysis

Essential theory

5.1 Introduction

The launch of a new product, an increase in manufacturing capacity, or perhaps the commissioning of a computerized accounts system are examples of major projects. In every case a major project management team will find it necessary to plan the project, and then control its execution.

These can be formidable tasks if the project is capital intensive, involves a complex set of interrelating factors, and if the success of the project is vital to long-term development. Further difficulties arise when it is necessary to coordinate a range of activities, each with its own demands upon managements' time and resources.

Network analysis has been developed specifically to assist the project manager to understand the ramifications for the project as a whole of the detailed arrangements of individual aspects. It is applied as a routine in large civil engineering projects. But there is hardly an area of industry or commerce which has not had recourse to network analysis at some time to assist the rational management of projects of every conceivable description.

A small-scale project has been chosen here as a vehicle for describing the methodology. Even so the reader may well come to a favourable judgement on the utility of the approach. We suppose that a company has decided to introduce a modern system of networked micros for automating the routine clerical tasks of an existing accounts office. This project clearly involves a range of preparatory activities. At the very least, these will include: the collection of information about suitable systems; the recruitment of systems analysts; the development of new accounting systems and procedures; training existing staff in the new methods; making arrangements to phase out the old and phase in the new; and organizing maintenance contracts for the new equipment.

These major project activities are listed in Table 5.1, where each activity is associated with an identifying index from 1 to 10. The table also records whether the start of any activity is dependent upon the prior completion of other activities. These 'Immediately Preceding Activities' (IPA) represent managements' considered opinion on how the activities interlock and interrelate with one another. Notice that some activities have no IPA, some have only one, and yet others have several. A final column gives the expected duration of each activity (in weeks).

Table 5.1   A dependency table for accounts office automation project

Index I	Activity	IPA	Duration T (weeks)
1	Draw up a short list of suitable systems	—	4
2	Appraise selected systems	1	8
3	Make a final choice of system	2	3
4	Order and obtain selected system	3	12
5	Develop new systems and procedures	3,8	24
6	Train staff in new procedures	4,5	8
7	Phase in the new procedures	6,9,10	4
8	Recruit systems analysts	—	6
9	Document the new procedures	5	12
10	Arrange maintenance contracts	3	5

The development of a dependency table like this is a major organizational challenge in itself. Success in a complex project, automating the routine procedures in the accounts office in this example, requires that the organization be capable both of generating the information on which to plan ahead, and of encouraging its people into new patterns of work.

The office automation project has been described in terms of 'activities' each of which require 'resources' (only time in this example), and which interrelate through a set of stated IPA. But the interrelation of activities listed in Table 5.1 can be more readily assimilated from a network diagram, as in Figure 5.1. Each node of this network diagram is a specified activity, and the arcs convey the sense in which the start of one activity depends upon the prior completion of all those in the IPA list.

Notice that the network diagram includes a 'start' and a 'finish' node. The start node is implicitly the preceding 'activity' to nodes 1 and 8 respectively, since these activities have no entry in their IPA lists and may be started without delay. Furthermore, all other activities have to be finished before activity 7 can commence, so it must follow that node 7 is the only IPA to the finish 'activity'. The arcs show the logical (dependency) relationships between the activities. The convention followed in Figure 5.1 is defined in Figure 5.2. The convention adopted here is to label with the

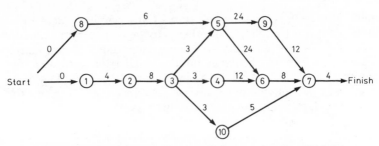

Figure 5.1 An activity on node network diagram: data from Table 5.1

duration of the activity any arc incident from the node associated with the activity. Thus the arcs incident *from* node 3 to nodes 4, 5, and 10 are labelled with the duration of activity 3 which is $T_3 = 3$ (weeks). The initial arcs are labelled with zero since activities 1 and 8 may commence immediately.

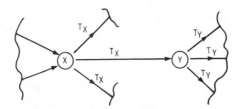

The completion of activity X precedes the start of Y
Activity X has duration T_X
Activity Y has duration T_Y

Figure 5.2 Labelling the arcs of an activity on node network diagram

The reader has probably noticed that the network of nodes is highly structured. That is to say that the network is *progressive*, that all the arcs are oriented from left to right; none is oriented vertically or from right to left. Therefore the *general progression* of the activities runs from start to finish. For an example, activity 8 must be completed before activity 5 is started, which awaits the completions in turn of activities 3, 2 and 1. But the relative timings of the start of the activities, cannot be inferred solely from the dispositions of the nodes on the network. The relative timings depend on the activity durations.

The network of Figure 5.1 displays sufficient information to *calculate* the Earliest Start Time (EST) and the Latest Start Time (LST) of every activity on the supposition that the project must be begun immediately and completed as soon as possible. The progressive character of the network ensures that simple arithmetic is all that is required (details are provided later). Note the convention for writing the calculated values of the EST and the LST above and below the activity nodes, as illustrated in Figure 5.3.

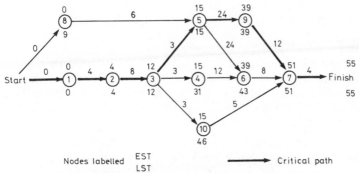

Figure 5.3 Activity on node network diagram, showing the EST, LST, and the critical path: data from Table 5.1

The project can be finished in a minimum period of 55 weeks. Activity 2 must start after 4 weeks, for example, whereas activity 8 can start at any time before the end of the ninth week.

When an activity has an earliest start time which coincides with its latest start time then any delay in its start will delay the earliest completion of the entire project. Such activities are described as 'critical', since management has no leeway in arranging the starting times. A 'critical path' from start to finish nodes through critical activities is shown in Figure 5.3 above. But note that in other examples there may be more than one critical path.

Activities not on the critical path(s) will have an EST which is earlier than the LST. The difference between the two is called 'total float' since management has, at a very maximum, this measure of discretion in varying the starting time. In fact there are several types of float (and the details are described later in Problem 5.7).

5.2 The construction of a progressive network

The calculation of EST and LST is a straightforward matter when the network is progressive. The network may be displayed on a monitor without ambiguity even when the arcs are shown as undirected edges. The method described below for the generation of a progressive network will also signal any contradictory logic which may be obscure but none the less present in the lists of IPA.

One can envisage a rectilinear grid of horizontal and vertical rulings with activities positioned only at the nodes, i.e. intersections. The idea is to locate the activities at the nodes on this grid, starting from the left-hand vertical ruling and working to the right. As many activities as possible are located on each vertical ruling while maintaining the convention of a progressive network, that the arcs which show the IPA logic must be oriented to the right.

The method is iterative, and successive iterations correspond to the allocation of activities to the nodes of successive vertical grid rulings. The iterations end when all the activities have been allocated. The algorithm can be described as follows:

Carry out the following two steps at each iteration:

Step 1. Locate activities at nodes of the current vertical ruling if and only if they have empty IPA lists (as reduced by step 2 in earlier iterations).

Step 2. Delete from all the IPA lists all those activities which have been located in step 1.

This algorithm (due to Fulkerson) is easy to carry out on the data of Table 5.1. A note is made of the activities which have been located in step 1 at each iteration, and deletions in step 2 can be shown by crossings out. A failure to locate any activity in step 1,

Table 5.2   The allocation of activities to the nodes of a progressive network, using the algorithm in the text and the data of Table 5.1

Activity		*Iteration (vertical ruling)*[c]						
	0[a]	1	2	3	4	5	6	7
1	—	—	—	—	—	—	—	—
2	1	~~1~~	—	—	—	—	—	—
3	2	2	~~2~~	—	—	—	—	—
4	3	3	3	~~3~~	—	—	—	—
5	3,8	3,~~8~~	3	~~3~~	—	—	—	—
6	4,5	4,5	4,5	4,5	~~4,5~~	—	—	—
7	6,9,10	6,9,10	6,9,10	6,9,10	6,9,~~10~~	~~6,9~~	—	—
8	—	—	—	—	—	—	—	—
9	5	5	5	5	~~5~~	—	—	—
10	3	3	3	~~3~~	—	—	—	—
Finish	7	7	7	7	7	7	~~7~~	—
Activities located in step 1[b]	start	1,8	2	3	4,5,10	6,9	7	finish

Notes: (a) The start node is trivially located at iteration 0, and is omitted from all the IPA to preserve clarity of presentation.

   (b) Assigned in index order to horizontal rulings about the horizontal axis of the network (one ruling above and then one below, two rulings above and then two below, etc.).

   (c) Deletions in step 2 indicated by crossings out.

when some one or more activities remain to be located, will indicate a contradictory dependency logic. Table 5.2 should be self-explanatory.

The reader can check that the bottom row of the table corresponds to the disposition of the nodes on Figures 5.1 and 5.3. The arcs can then be drawn from each activity in accordance with the original IPA list.

If you try to construct a progressive network for the data in Table 5.3 it soon becomes apparent that the lists of IPA are mutually contradictory.

Table 5.3 Demonstration of the algorithm on a set of inconsistent data

Data		Algorithm		
				Iteration
Activity	IPA	Activity	0	1
1	2	1	2	2
2	3	2	3	3
3	1	3	1	1
		Locate	start	?

Program PROGNET is designed to carry out the algorithm described above. It consists of a short main program which dimensions arrays in order to accept up to 100 activities and up to 10 IPA per activity. It sequences PROCinput, PROCterminal and PROCreorder as follows:

PROCinput: allows the user to input the dependency table for activity Y, for Y = 1, 2, . . . , N. Each activity Y has an IPA list which is stored in an array PREC(Y,I) and the element PREC(Y,O) stores the number of preceding activities. IMAX is set equal to the maximum of the PREC(Y,O) over all Y. Elements of an array TERMINAL(X) are set to −1 for any activity X which is contained in the union of activities in the separate IPA lists.

PROCterminal: accumulates the set of IPA for the Finished node N + 1 in PREC(N + 1,I), where I = 1, 2, . . . , PREC(N + 1, O).

PROCreorder: controls the iterative nature of the algorithm via the variable IT, which corresponds to the index of the vertical grid ruling. Calls PROCstep1 at each iteration, and locates the Finished node N + 1 on completion. Calls PROCrestore.

PROCstep1:   corresponds to the description of step 1 in the
                      text above, using the test PREC(Y,O) = O
                      whereupon an activity Y, say, is assigned to an
                      array NODE(IT,K), where the index K corres-
                      ponds to a horizontal grid ruling. Further arrays
                      IT(Y) and K(Y) store 'the x and y coordinates'
                      IT and K of the node for activity Y. Updates
                      KMAX the maximum value of K found to date.
                      Prints 'infeasible network' as appropriate or
                      calls PROCstep2 for every unassigned activity.
PROCstep2:   corresponds to the description of step 2 in the
                      text above; deletion of the activity Y from the
                      IPA list of activity X is achieved by reversing the
                      sign of the element storing Y in the array
                      PREC(X,I), and the value of PREC(X,O) is
                      reduced accordingly.
PROCrestore: restores the array PREC(Y,I) to its earlier
                      condition following PROCinput.

Type in PROGNET from the listing below.

Program 5.1 PROGNET: Assigns activities to nodes of a progressive network

```
10 REM PROGNET
20 REM SEQUENCES ACTIVITIES BY FULKERSON'S APPROACH
30 REM FOR AN ACTIVITY ON NODE PLANNING NETWORK
40 REM IN ORDER TO CONSTRUCT A PROGRESSIVE NETWORK
50 DIM PREC(100,10),NODE(10,10),IT(100),K(100),TERMINAL(100)
60
70 PROCinput
80 PROCterminal
90 PROCreorder
100 END
110
1000 DEF PROCinput
1010 INPUT "HOW MANY ACTIVITIES ",N
1020 PRINT "NOW INPUT THE PRECEDENCE RELATIONSHIPS"
1030 PRINT "ON EACH PROMPT ENTER A PRECEDING ACTIVITY"
1040 PRINT "ENTER ZERO WHEN NONE REMAIN"
1050 PRINT : PRINT "  ACTIVITY     PREDECESSOR"
1055 IMAX=0 : KMAX=0
1060 FOR Y= 1 TO N
1070 I=0 : PRINT
1080 PRINT Y;
1090 REPEAT
1100 I=I+1
1110 INPUT TAB(25) X
1120 IF X>0 THEN PREC(Y,0)=PREC(Y,0)+1
1130 IF X>0 THEN PREC(Y,I)=X : TERMINAL(X)=-1
1140 UNTIL X=0
1150 IF I>IMAX THEN IMAX=I
1170 NEXT Y
1180 PRINT
1190 ENDPROC
1200
```

```
1500 DEF PROCterminal
1510 I=0
1520 FOR X= 1 TO N
1530 IF TERMINAL(X)=0 THEN I=I+1 : PREC(N+1,I)=X
1540 NEXT X
1550 PREC(N+1,0)=I
1560 ENDPROC
1570
2000 DEF PROCreorder
2010 Z=0 : IT=0 : IT(0)=0 : K(0)=1
2020 REPEAT
2030 PRINT : IT=IT+1
2040 PROCstep1
2050 UNTIL Z=N
2060 NODE(IT+1,1)=N+1
2070 NODE(IT+1,0)=1
2080 PROCrestore
2090 ENDPROC
2100
2500 DEF PROCrestore
2510 FOR Y= 1 TO N
2520 J=0
2530 FOR I= 1 TO IMAX
2540 IF PREC(Y,I)<0 THEN J=J+1
2550 IF PREC(Y,I)<0 THEN PREC(Y,I)=-PREC(Y,I)
2560 NEXT I
2570 PREC(Y,0)=J
2580 NEXT Y
2590 ENDPROC
2600
3000 DEF PROCstep1
3010 K=0 : PRINT "REORDERING ITERATION ";IT
3020 FOR Y= 1 TO N
3030 IF PREC(Y,0)=0 THEN K=K+1 : PRINT Y;" AT NODE ";IT;",";K
3040 IF PREC(Y,0)=0 THEN Z=Z+1 :NODE(IT,K)=Y :IT(Y)=IT :K(Y)=K
3050 IF PREC(Y,0)=0 THEN PREC(Y,0)=-1
3060 NEXT Y
3070 NODE(IT,0)=K
3080 IF K>KMAX THEN KMAX=K
3090 IF K=0 THEN PRINT "INFEASIBLE NETWORK" : END
3100 FOR X= 1 TO N
3110 IF PREC(X,0) > 0 THEN PROCstep2
3120 NEXT X
3130 ENDPROC
3140
4000 DEF PROCstep2
4010 FOR k= 1 TO K
4020 FOR I= 1 TO IMAX
4030 IF PREC(X,I)=NODE(IT,k) THEN PREC(X,0)=PREC(X,0)-1
4040 IF PREC(X,I)=NODE(IT,k) THEN PREC(X,I)=-PREC(X,I)
4050 NEXT I
4060 NEXT k
4070 ENDPROC
4080
```

When satisfied with the accuracy of your listing you should RUN
with the data of Table 5.1. Note that a zero is entered to indicate
the end of each list of IPA (pressing the RETURN key enters a
zero on the BBC Micro). The output corresponds to the results in
the lower half of Table 5.2, and the grid is displayed in Figure 5.4.

70

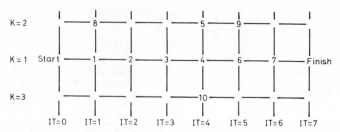

Figure 5.4 Assignment of activities to nodes of a progressive network: data from Table 5.1

```
 RUN
HOW MANY ACTIVITIES ?10
NOW INPUT THE PRECEDENCE RELATIONSHIPS
ON EACH PROMPT ENTER A PRECEDING ACTIVITY
ENTER ZERO WHEN NONE REMAIN

   ACTIVITY      PREDECESSOR

        1              0

        2              1
                       0

        3              2
                       0

        4              3
                       0

        5              3
                       8
                       0

        6              4
                       5
                       0

        7              6
                       9
                      10
                       0

        8              0

        9              5
                       0

       10              3
                       0


REORDERING ITERATION 1
        1 AT NODE 1,1
        8 AT NODE 1,2

REORDERING ITERATION 2
        2 AT NODE 2,1

REORDERING ITERATION 3
        3 AT NODE 3,1
```

```
REORDERING ITERATION 4
        4 AT NODE 4,1
        5 AT NODE 4,2
       10 AT NODE 4,3

REORDERING ITERATION 5
        6 AT NODE 5,1
        9 AT NODE 5,2

REORDERING ITERATION 6
        7 AT NODE 6,1
```

The reader should now do Problem 5.1.

5.3 Earliest and latest start analyses

It is a simple matter to calculate the Earliest Start Time (EST) for each activity. The start of activity Y, say, must be preceded by the completion of each immediately preceding activity. It follows that

$$EST_Y = MAX_{X \in IPA \text{ of } Y}\{EST_X + T_X\} \text{ where } EST_0 = 0$$
$$= EST_{P(Y)} + T_{P(Y)}$$

where $P(Y)$ is written for the 'maximizing' X. (Note that $P(Y)$ need not be unique.)

Since the activities are assigned to the nodes of a progressive network, the EST could be calculated recursively, from the left-hand vertical ruling to the right-hand vertical ruling. Alternatively, the EST calculation can be made immediately an activity is assigned to a node of the progressive network. Taking either approach one would find for the data in Figure 5.1 that

$$
\begin{aligned}
&EST_0 = 0 \\
&EST_1 = EST_0 + 0 = 0 &&: P_1 = 0 \\
&EST_8 = EST_0 + 0 = 0 &&: P_8 = 0 \\
&EST_2 = EST_1 + T_1 = 4 &&: P_2 = 1 \\
&EST_3 = EST_2 + T_2 = 12 &&: P_3 = 2 \\
&EST_4 = EST_3 + T_3 = 15 &&: P_4 = 3 \\
&EST_5 = MAX\{EST_3 + T_3; EST_8 + T_8\} = 15 &&: P_5 = 3 \\
&EST_{10} = EST_3 + T_3 = 15 &&: P_{10} = 3 \\
&EST_6 = MAX\{EST_4 + T_4; EST_5 + T_5\} = 39 &&: P_6 = 5 \\
&EST_9 = EST_5 + T_5 = 39 &&: P_9 = 5 \\
&EST_7 = MAX\{EST_6 + T_6; EST_9 + T_9; EST_{10} + T_{10}\} = 51 &&: P_7 = 9 \\
&EST_{11} = EST_7 + T_7 = 55 &&: P_{11} = 7
\end{aligned}
$$

It is now easy to trace the critical path back from node $(N + 1)$. In the present example this gives the unique sequence.

$$P_{11} = 7 \quad P_7 = 9 \quad P_9 = 5 \quad P_5 = 3 \quad P_3 = 2 \quad P_2 = 1$$

Suppose that activity Z is an Immediately Succeeding Activity (ISA) to activity Y. Then the Latest Start Time, LST_Y, of activity Y is given by

$$LST_Y = MIN \{LST_Z - T_Y\} \quad \text{where } LST_{N+1} = EST_{N+1}$$
$$Z \; \epsilon \; \text{ISA of Y}$$

This follows the recognition that LST_Y must be the smallest sum $LST_Z - T_Y$. These calculations proceed recursively across the progressive network from the right to the left. In the present example based on Figure 5.1 one finds

$$LST_{11} = 55$$
$$LST_7 = LST_{11} - T_7 = 51$$
$$LST_6 = LST_7 - T_6 = 43$$
$$LST_9 = LST_7 - T_9 = 39$$
$$LST_4 = LST_6 - T_4 = 31$$
$$LST_5 = MIN\{LST_6 - T_5; LST_9 - T_5\} = 15$$
$$LST_{10} = LST_7 - T_{10} = 46$$
$$LST_3 = MIN\{LST_4 - T_3; LST_5 - T_3; LST_{10} - T_3\} = 12$$
$$LST_2 = LST_3 - T_2 = 4$$
$$LST_1 = LST_2 - T_1 = 0$$
$$LST_8 = LST_5 - T_8 = 9$$

Make the following changes and additions to PROGNET. The resulting program, called CRITPAT, allows the user to input the activity duration into array T prior to inputting the list of IPA. Three new PROCEDURES, PROCearliest_start, PROClatest_ start and PROCprint are called at the end of the main program.PROCearliest_start and PROClatest_start are based very closely upon the description of the calculations of EST and LST. PROCprint is an output procedure which tabulates the activities which have been assigned to each node of the progressive network. It also prints a list of EST, LST and total float.

```
  10 REM CRITPAT
  20 REM CONDUCTS EARLIEST AND LATEST START TIME ANALYSIS
  30 REM FOR AN ACTIVITY ON NODE PLANNING NETWORK
  40 REM AND FINDS A CRITICAL PATH

  60 DIM P(100),EST(100) ,T(100),LST(100)

 100 PROCearliest_start
 110 PROClatest_start
 120 PROCprint
 130 END
 140

1050 PRINT : PRINT " ACTIVITY  DURATION PREDECESSOR"

1070 I=0 : LST(Y)=10^10
1080 PRINT Y; : INPUT TAB(19) T(Y)

1110 INPUT TAB(31) X

5000 DEF PROCearliest_start
5010 VDU 5
5020 FOR it= 1 TO IT+1
5030 FOR k = 1 TO NODE(it,0)
5040 Y=NODE(it,k)
5050 FOR I= 1 TO PREC(Y,0)
5060 X=PREC(Y,I)
5070 IF X<>0 THEN IF EST(Y)<EST(X)+T(X) THEN P(Y)=X
5080 IF X<>0 THEN IF EST(Y)<EST(X)+T(X) THEN EST(Y)=EST(X)+T(X)
5090 NEXT I
5100 NEXT k
5110 NEXT it
5120 ENDPROC
5130
6000 DEF PROClatest_start
6010 LST(N+1)=EST(N+1)
6020 FOR it = IT+1 TO 2 STEP -1
6030 FOR k = 1 TO NODE(it,0)
6040 Y=NODE(it,k)
6050 FOR I= 1 TO PREC(Y,0)
6060 X=PREC(Y,I)
6070 IF X<>0 THEN IF LST(X)>LST(Y)-T(X) THEN LST(X)=LST(Y)-T(X)
6080 NEXT I
6090 NEXT k
6100 NEXT it
6110 ENDPROC
6120
6500 DEF PROCprint
6510 PRINT : PRINT "ITERATION      INDEX  ACTIVITY"
6520 PRINT TAB(3) "it";TAB(17) "k"
6530 FOR it=1 TO IT
6540 FOR k=1 TO NODE(it,0)
6550 PRINT TAB(4); it;TAB(17);k;TAB(25);NODE(it,k)
6560 NEXT k
6570 NEXT it
6580 PRINT : PRINT
6590 PRINT "ACTIVITY      EARLIEST    LATEST      FLOAT"
6600 PRINT "              START       START"
6610 PRINT "    Y         EST(Y)      LST(Y)    LST-EST"
6620 FOR Y=1 TO N
6630 PRINT TAB(3);Y;TAB(15) EST(Y);TAB(26) LST(Y);TAB(36) LST(Y)-EST(Y)
6640 NEXT Y
6650 PRINT "FINISH";TAB(15) EST(N+1);TAB(26) LST(N+1);TAB(36) "0"
6660 PRINT : PRINT
6670 PRINT "CRITICAL PATH"
6680 Y=P(N+1)
6690 REPEAT
6700 PRINT Y,
6710 Y=P(Y)
6720 UNTIL Y=0
6730 ENDPROC
```

RUN this program, called 'CRITPAT', with the data of Table 5.1, noting that the activity duration is requested prior to the list of IPA. The final part of the output, which is shown below, corresponds to the results obtained earlier in this section. You should note that this program ignores the possibility of multiple critical paths, and this aspect is left as an exercise. Do Problems 5.3 to 5.7 now.

ITERATION	INDEX	ACTIVITY
it	k	
1	1	1
1	2	8
2	1	2
3	1	3
4	1	4
4	2	5
4	3	10
5	1	6
5	2	9
6	1	7

ACTIVITY	EARLIEST START	LATEST START	FLOAT
Y	EST(Y)	LST(Y)	LST-EST
1	0	0	0
2	4	4	0
3	12	12	0
4	15	31	16
5	15	15	0
6	39	43	4
7	51	51	0
8	0	9	9
9	39	39	0
10	15	46	31
FINISH	55	55	0

```
CRITICAL PATH
        7
        9
        5
        3
        2
        1
```

5.4 Graphics output

It is obviously desirable to have a network displayed on the monitor, at least for small illustrative examples. The following procedures produce a graphics output which resembles the network diagram of Figure 5.3. The general approach is to offer the user the option of a graphics output; flag G$ = 'Y' if graphics are required. If it transpires that more than five horizontal or eight vertical grid rulings are necessary, then the graphics option is withdrawn automatically, and flag G$ = 'N'.

The activity indices are placed on the network grid in

PROCdraw_activities, and the network logic is plotted in PROCdraw_logic. Both these procedures are called from PROCearliest_start. PROCscreen_driver halts the graphics display and the user can proceed at his leisure by a tap on the space bar. This activates PROCdraw_times which displays the EST and LST alongside the nodes, and a further tap of the space bar activates PROCdraw_crit_path. A final tap of the space bar yields the tabular print summary of PROCprint.

Make the following changes and additions to Program CRITPAT

```
 10 REM NETWORK
 20 REM DRAWS ACTIVITIES AND NETWORK LOGIC
 30 REM FOR AN ACTIVITY ON NODE NETWORK
 40 REM DISPLAYS TIME ANALYSIS AND A CRITICAL PATH

100 MODE 4 :PROCearliest_start
110 PROClatest_start
120 IF G$<>"N" THEN PROCscreen_driver
130 IF G$<>"N" THEN PROCdraw_times
140 IF G$<>"N" THEN PROCscreen_driver
150 IF G$<>"N" THEN PROCdraw_crit_path
160 IF G$<>"N" THEN PROCscreen_driver
170 MODE 7 : PROCprint
180 END
190

1180 PRINT : INPUT "GRAPHICAL OUTPUT? (Y OR N) ",G$
1190 ENDPROC
1200

2090 IF IT>8 THEN G$="N"
2100 ENDPROC
2110

3080 IF K>KMAX THEN KMAX=K :IF K>7 THEN G$="N"

5045 IF G$<>"N" THEN PROCdraw_activity

5065 IF it=1 AND G$<>"N" THEN PROCdraw_logic
5066 IF X<>0 AND G$<>"N" THEN PROCdraw_logic

7000 DEF PROCdraw_activity
7010 MOVE FNx(it),FNy(k) : PRINT STR$(Y)
7020 ENDPROC
7030
7500 DEF PROCdraw_logic
7510 MOVE FNx(it)-16,FNy(k)-16
7520 PLOT 29,FNx(IT(X))+64,FNy(K(X))-16
7530 ENDPROC
7540
7800 DEF PROCscreen_driver
7810 MOVE 0,24 : PRINT "PRESS SPACE BAR TO CONTINUE"
7820 REPEAT : UNTIL GET$=" "
7830 ENDPROC
7840
```

```
8000 DEF PROCdraw_times
8010 FOR  it= 1 TO IT+1
8020 FOR k= 1 TO NODE(it,0)
8030 MOVE FNx(it),FNy(k)+32
8040 T=EST(NODE(it,k))
8050 PRINT STR$(T)
8060 MOVE FNx(it),FNy(k)-32
80/0 T=LST(NODE(it,k))
8080 PRINT STR$(T)
8090 NEXT k
8100 NEXT it
8110 ENDPROC
8120
8500 DEF PROCdraw_crit_path
8510 X=N+1 : IT(N+1)=IT+1 :k=1
8520 REPEAT
8530 Y=X
8540 it=IT(Y) : k=K(Y)
8550 MOVE FNx(it)-12,FNy(k)-12
8560 X=P(Y)
8570 PLOT 13,FNx(IT(X))+68,FNy(K(X))-12
8580 UNTIL IT(X)=1
8590 ENDPROC
8600
9000 DEF FNx(it)
9010 XAXIS=528+(-1)^it*INT(it/2)*16
9020 =INT(1216/(IT+1))*it
9030
9500 DEF FNy(k)
9510 IF KMAX=1 THEN KMAX=3
9520 IF INT(KMAX/2)=KMAX/2 THEN KMAX=KMAX+1
9530 DELTAY=INT(854/(KMAX-1))
9540 IF INT(k/2)=k/2 THEN =XAXIS+DELTAY*k/2
9550 IF INT(k/2)<>k/2 THEN =XAXIS+DELTAY*(.5-k/2)
```

A RUN of this program, called NETWORK, should give the screen display of Figure 5.5. It is reasonably clear, but reRUNs with other data may perhaps lead to some of the arcs passing very close by some of the nodes. The 'x-axis' has been perturbed so that nodes which would have lain on the same horizontal grid ruling have some vertical separation. This is a necessary if not sufficient condition if the network logic is to be displayed in an unambiguous manner. You should do the rest of the Problems at this point.

5.5 Discussion

The type of network which has been described here is called 'activity on node', for fairly obvious reasons. An alternative form is called 'activity on arrow' but although it is popular it has one major disadvantage: it is sometimes necessary to introduce dummy activities (arrows) in order to preserve the network logic. This can make it difficult to write a clear BASIC program in a reasonable amount of code. Otherwise the choice between the two methods is largely made on the grounds of individual preference, rather than fundamental differences in capability.

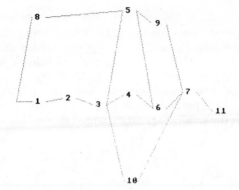

PRESS SPACE BAR TO CONTINUE

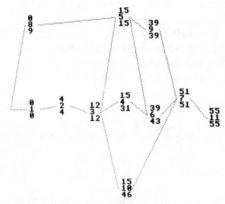

PRESS SPACE BAR TO CONTINUE

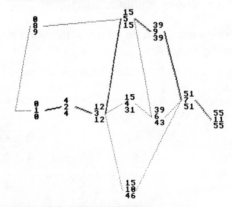

PRESS SPACE BAR TO CONTINUE

Figure 5.5 A sequence of screen displays

The question of the resource implications of any schedule of activities is very important in the business context.But algorithms for resource levelling and smoothing are outside the scope of this chapter. Nevertheless, this chapter should have served to introduce the reader to network analysis by computer. A large number of fairly sophisticated software packages are now available, but perhaps few packages offer such convenient graphics as the small program described above.

Problems

(5.1) Devise a PROCdata which can be exercised at the user's discretion to read data from DATA statements as an alternative to conversational data input in PROCinput.

(5.2) Devise a PROCsensitivity to be called at line 180 of NETWORK. This should allow the user to alter any part of the input data for subsequent re-processing, as part of a REPEAT-UNTIL loop between lines 65 and 190.

(5.3) Use your amended program from Problem 5.1 to conduct a network analysis when the minimum activity times are revised downward from the maximum shown in Table 1 as follows:

Activity	1	2	3	4	5	6	7	8	9	10
Minimum duration	2	4	1	4	10	4	2	4	9	3

(5.4) Consider the ways in which one could develop NETWORK to print out and display multiple critical paths.

(5.5) Classify each stage in the office automation project into one of the following categories:

Definitely not critical: Possibly critical: Definitely critical

(5.6) Now suppose that the 'most likely' duration is available for the activities. The data is now:

Activity	1	2	3	4	5	6	7	8	9	10
Minimum time	2	4	1	4	10	4	2	4	9	3
Most likely time	3	5	2	10	19	7	3	5	10	4
Maximum time	4	8	3	12	24	8	4	6	12	5

It can be shown, subject to the possibly realistic assumption that the activity durations are drawn from a set of independent random variables which follow a beta distribution, that the project duration has an expected value μ and variance σ^2

where $\mu = \Sigma t_Y$
$\sigma^2 = \Sigma \sigma_Y^2$

where the Σ is taken over all the critical activities Y

and $t_Y = (4\,ML_Y + MIN_Y + MAX_Y)/6$
$\sigma_Y^2 = (MAX_Y - MIN_Y)^2/36$

where ML   is the most likely duration of an activity
MIN   is the minimum duration of an activity
MAX is the maximum duration of an activity.

Devise a PROCpert which evaluates the standard normal deviate

$z = (x - \mu)/\sigma$

for a user input value of x. The reader can then determine the associated probability that the project is completed on time.

N.B. This estimated probability is an upper bound, since any activity with a highly variable duration which is off the critical path, *on average*, could well become critical in a particular instance.

(5.7) The Earliest Finish Time (EFT_Y) and the Latest Finish Time (LFT_Y) of activity Y are given by

$EFT_Y = EST_Y + T_Y$
$LFT_Y = LST_Y + T_Y$

The management has discretion to delay the starting time of an activity Y, without affecting the total float of subsequent activities Z, by an amount called the Free Float FF_Y, where

$FF_Y = MIN\{EST_Z\} - EFT_Y$
$\quad\quad Z \,\varepsilon\, ISA_Y$

and the minimization is taken over all immediately succeeding activities Z.

The management may have discretion to vary the start of an activity Y, without affecting the activities X which precede Y or activities Z which succeed Y, by an amount called the Independent Float IF_Y, where

$IF_Y = MIN\{EST_Z\} - MAX\{LFT_X\} - T_Y$
$\quad\quad Z \,\varepsilon\, ISA_Y \quad\quad X \,\varepsilon\, IPA_Y$

and the minimization is over all immediately succeeding activities Z, and the maximization is over all immediately preceding X.

Devise a PROCfloats which tabulates the EFT and LFT times alongside the EST and LST, and tabulates the three types of float.

(5.8) Devise a PROCresources which tabulates the growth in cumulative cashflows week by week, on the assumption that all activities commence at their EST. Use your program to analyse the following project.

A company is preparing to launch a new product at a forthcoming trade show. The product manager has drawn up the following dependency table, which also includes cost and duration data:

Activity		Duration (weeks)	Cost (£'000)	List of IPA
1	Train salesmen	3	6	3,10
2	Train service engineers	4	8	3,9
3	Prepare automation manuals	10	3	—
4	Organize trade show	4	2	7,10
5	Train staff for trade show	1	0.5	4
6	Pre-release publicity	3	6	8,10
7	Recruit staff for show	2	0.2	8
8	Set up sales office	5	4.5	—
9	Prepare service contract	5	3	—
10	Produce promotional materials	8	12	9

(5.9) Devise a PROCswop to interchange the indices of a pair of activities which have been assigned to the same vertical grid ruling, as a PROCsensitivity facility. Then reRUN Problem 5.8 with a swop of activity indices 4 and 6. Notice that this is ideal for improving the appearance of the network.

Chapter 6

Linear programming

Essential theory

The term 'linear programme' is given to a particular type of constrained optimization problem. It is assumed explicitly that there is a linear form of objective; say minimize the raw material costs of production, or maximize the contribution of some activity to overheads and profit. It is also explicitly assumed that the optimization of the objective function is subject to linear constraints. Constraints result from a multitude of factors. A constraint may be due to scarce resources such as a restriction upon working capital, or a contractual obligation to supply a certain quantity of product.

The simplest linear programme has the form,

$$Maximize\ z = bx_1 + b_2x_2 + \ldots \qquad + b_nx_n$$
$$Subject\ to\ a_{1,1}x_1 + a_{1,2}x_2 + \ldots + a_{1,n}x_n < = c_1$$
$$a_{2,1}x_1 + a_{2,2}x_2 + \ldots \quad + a_{2,n}x_n <= c_2$$
$$\ldots$$
$$\ldots$$
$$a_{m,1}x_1 + a_{m,2}x_2 + \ldots + a_{m,n}x_n <= c_n$$
$$for\ x_1 > = 0 \quad x_2 >= 0 \ldots x_n >= 0$$

There are n main variables, sometimes called decision variables. There are m linear inequality constraints which are written such that the left-hand sides are less than or equal to the non-negative right-hand side values (c_i in the ith inequality). The main variables x_j for $j = 1,2, \ldots ,n$ are subject to explicit non-negativity restrictions, but it is important to appreciate the convention that these are *excluded* from the count of m linear constraints *per se*. On occasion the constraints are mixed, i.e. include linear equality constraints, and linear inequality constraints where the left-hand side exceeds the non-negative right. These features are discussed later.

Consider the following numerical example, which is deliberately chosen for simplicity rather than realism. A division of a company manufactures two main products, type 1 and 2. The number of

81

items produced per period is x_1 and x_2 respectively. If it is assumed that all the output can be sold and that the contribution to profit and overhead is 3 and 1 monetary unit (mu) per item of type 1 and 2 respectively, then the objective, to maximize the total contribution, z, can be written

Maximize $z = 3x_1 + 1x_2$

However, there is a limit on working capital of 500 mu in the period in question. The manufacture of each item requires 2 and 1 mu of working capital respectively, and so there is an inequality constraint of the form

$2x_1 + x_2 <= 500$

Furthermore, the second product incorporates proprietary bought-in items with an extended reorder lead time. The current stockholding is sufficient for the production of a maximum of 200 items of the second product. Thus there is a second constraint of the form

$x_2 <= 200$

To summarize, the linear programme can be written

Maximize	$z = 3x_1 +$	x_2	Objective function
subject to	$2x_1 +$	$x_2 <= 500$	Working capital
		$x_2 <= 200$	Bought-in items
	x_1 and	$x_2 >= 0$	Non-negativity

This problem, which will be referred to as P1 for brevity, can be portrayed graphically as follows. The two main variables are each allocated to an axis of Figure 6.1 The non-negativity restrictions are shown by the hatching on the 'forbidden' sides of the axes (i.e. the hatching below the x_1 axis corresponds to the stipulation that $x_2 >= 0$).

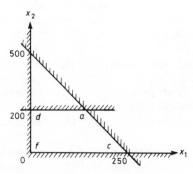

Figure 6.1 Constraints of P1

Take the case of the bought-in item constraint: this is represented by the horizontal line which intersects the vertical axis at $x_2 = 200$, i.e. whatever the x_1 value may be the value of x_2 must not exceed 200. To see how the 'working capital' constraint is represented it is sufficient to appreciate that the boundary between production plans which cost more or less than 500 mu is represented by the equation

$$2x_1 + x_2 = 500$$

This linear equation can be represented by a straight line. The x_2 intercept can be found from the equation with $x_1 = 0$ and the x_1 intercept can be found from the equation with $x_2 = 0$. The line in Figure 6.1 joining these two points is hatched from above. The origin, the point representing a failure to manufacture any products at all, obviously satisfies the restriction upon working capital. So it can be argued that *all* points 'below' the line satisfy the restriction.

Any point lying within or upon the boundary of the hatched region represents a combination of x_1 and x_2 which is feasible with respect to the non-negativity restrictions, the availability of working capital, and the availability of bought-in items. The area fcad so defined is called the *feasible region*.

It can be shown that one (or more) of the vertices formed by an intersection of the constraint boundaries will always optimize a linear objective function. To see this, note that a profit contribution of, say, 500 mu can be represented by

$$3x_1 + x_2 = 500$$

This line can be added to Figure 6.2, where it is seen to cross the feasible region. It is clear that any point which lies both on the line

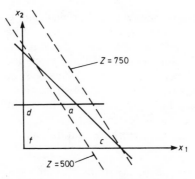

Figure 6.2 Superimposing the objective

and within the feasible region corresponds to a possible production plan not exceeding available resources. But other lines with different right-hand side values will be parallel. When the right-hand side is 750 the objective line intersects vertex c as shown in the figure. So it is possible to realize a contribution of 750 only if the unique production plan $x_1 = 250$ and $x_2 = 0$ is adhered to. It is also clear that this is the optimum contribution since the objective line with a right-hand side of 751 or more must lie wholly outside the feasible region.

The coefficients of the objective function merely determine the orientation of the family of objective function lines over the feasible region. The sense of optimization (i.e. maximization or minimization) determines which is the preferred line. In all cases however a vertex will provide an optimum solution. The case of multiple optima is considered later.

6.1 A solution by complete enumeration of the vertices

In principle, the coordinates of each vertex and the corresponding value of the objective function could be calculated in turn, as shown in Table 6.1, and the vertex c is once again selected as the optimum solution.

Table 6.1   Vertex enumeration for problem P1

Vertex	x_1	x_2	z
a	150	200	650
c	250	0	750
d	0	200	200
f	0	0	0

N.B. Vertices are indexed lexicographically, as later explained.

Problem P1 was amenable to graphical analysis only because there were just two main variables, x_1 and x_2. When there are large numbers of main variables x_j for $j = 1, 2, \ldots n$ it is clearly impossible to envisage the feasible region physically modelled in any way. But the algebraic concept of a 'basis' is always equivalent to the geometric concept of a vertex. To illustrate this idea for problem P1 it is necessary only to restate the inequality constraints as equations. 'Slack' variables x_3 and x_4 are introduced into the left-hand side of the working capital and bought-in item inequalities.

$$2x_1 + x_2 + x_3 \quad\ = 500 \quad \text{Working capital}$$
$$x_2 + \quad\ x_4 = 200 \quad \text{Bought-in items}$$

The slack variables are explicitly taken to be non-negative. The numerical value of a slack variable is the amount by which the actual resources usage, as expressed by the left-hand side of the constraint, falls short of the resource availability, given by the right-hand side value. If $x_1 = x_2 = 0$ then the slack variables are numerically $x_3 = 500$ and $x_4 = 200$. But as the main variables x_1 and x_2 are increased so the value of each slack variable reduces to maintain the equality. Further increases in a main variable are prevented when a slack variable reaches zero, either because all the working capital has been employed or the bought-in items have been used up.

Figure 6.3 shows how each boundary of the feasible region is associated with an individual zero-valued variable. Away from a boundary and within the feasible region the corresponding slack or main variable will be positive.

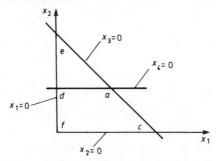

Figure 6.3 Labelling the boundaries and vertices of problem P1

Consequently the vertices in Figure 6.3 correspond to certain pairs of zero-valued variables, as indicated in the second column of Table 6.2. At vertex c, for instance, $x_2 = x_3 = 0$. Furthermore, x_1 and x_4 are positive since vertex c is distant from the boundaries at which these variables are zero. There are altogether $^4C_2$ combinations of two positive and two zero-valued variables and these are enumerated in Table 6.2.

Table 6.2   Lexicographic vertex enumeration

Variables which are	non-zero (basis)	Vertex	Variables = 0	
$x_1 = 150$	$x_2 = 200$	a	x_3	x_4
x_1	x_3	none	x_2	x_4
$x_1 = 250$	$x_4 = 200$	c	x_2	x_3
$x_2 = 200$	$x_3 = 300$	d	x_1	x_4
$x_2 = 500$	$x_4 = -300$	e	x_1	x_3
$x_3 = 500$	$x_4 = 200$	f	x_1	x_2

Two important observations can be made here. First, the list contains all vertices, even obviously infeasible ones, such as vertex *e* which lies outside the feasible region (see Figure 6.3). Second, not all the expected vertices even exist. There is no vertex *b* since the constraint boundaries along which x_2 and x_4 are zero do not intersect, and it is clear that the corresponding equations could never be satisfied:

$$2x_1 + x_3 = 500$$
$$0x_1 + 0x_3 = 200$$

i.e. the matrix of coefficients is *singular*.

The two zero-valued variables, at each feasible vertex, are termed *non-basic* variables. Since there are four variables altogether there are also two non-zero variables, termed *basic* variables. Basic variables are known collectively as the *basis*. Each feasible vertex has a feasible basis. In summary, when there are two variables and two constraints there are no more than $^4C_2$ feasible vertices, each with an associated basis.

Now suppose that two additional constraints are added to problem P1. Products 1 and 2 require 1 and 2 units of assembly time respectively, and to ensure 'normal time' working of 400 or more units of assembly time we find a third constraint

$$x_1 + 2x_2 >= 400 \qquad \text{Normal time}$$

Furthermore, the first product is made on a continuous process and management are reluctant to slow the process down below an output of 100 units over the planning period. Thus

$$x_1 \qquad >= 100 \qquad \text{Process constraint}$$

The enlarged problem can then be written

Maximize $3x_1 + x_2$ Obj. function
subject to $2x_1 + x_2 <= 500$ Working capital
$\qquad\qquad x_2 <= 200$ Bought-in items
$\qquad x_1 + 2x_2 >= 400$ Normal time working
$\qquad x_1 \qquad >= 100$ Process constraint
$\qquad x_1$ and $x_2 >= 0$ Non-negativity

This problem, which will be referred to as P2, is represented in Figure 6.4. The feasible region of problem P1 is now further constrained. It seems from Figure 6.4 that the vertices again correspond, with one exception, to the idea of two intersecting boundaries of the feasible region, and thus to two zero-valued variables. Notice, however, that the vertices labelled 3, 12 and 13 are in fact coincident. This is a consequence of the intersection of three rather than two constraint boundaries. Consideration of this feature, termed *degeneracy*, will be postponed. But it can be seen that an optimum solution can be sought either through a complete enumeration of the vertices, or by superimposing the family of objective function lines: vertex 5 is the optimum vertex here.

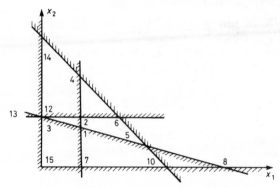

Figure 6.4 Graphical representation of problem P2

In order to investigate the problem further subtract non-zero 'surplus' variables x_5 and x_6 from the left-hand sides of the new constraints. The constraint set then becomes

$$
\begin{aligned}
2x_1 + x_2 + x_3 & & & = 500 \\
x_2 & + x_4 & & = 200 \\
x_1 + 2x_2 & - x_5 & & = 400 \\
x_1 & - x_6 & & = 100
\end{aligned}
$$

Since there are now six variables altogether and two must be zero at a vertex we search for bases with $6-2 = 4$ non-zero, or basic variables. There are $^6C_4 = 15$ ways of selecting 4 variables from 6. The figure clearly shows only four vertices in the feasible region and so we expect four feasible bases altogether. In general, with n main variables and m constraints we have a maximum of $^{m+n}C_n$ vertices and it is usual for only a small proportion of these to be feasible; as always, each feasible vertex gives rise to a feasible basis.

Program VERTEX is designed to list the $^{m+n}C_m$ combinations of variables which are basis candidates. The list is in lexicographic order of the variables (a standard dictionary contains words in lexicographic order). The main program calls the following PROCEDURES:

PROCinput: allows the user to enter the total number of variables including the main, slack, and surplus variables, together with the number of constraints.

PROCbasis: selects the first M variables as an initial basis candidate set and generates successive candidates in lexicographic order.

PROCprint: prints the candidate basis.

A RUN of this program yields the 15 candidates bases for problem P2, which has 6 variables and 4 constraints. The index numbers of the candidate bases correspond to the indexing of the vertices in Figure 6.4.

Program 6.1 VERTEX: Generates basic variable sets for all bases

```
   5 REM VERTEX
  10 REM CANDIDATE BASIC VARIABLE SETS IN LEXICOGRAPHIC ORDER
  20 V=0
  30 @%=&020210
  40 DIM K(10)
  50 PROCinput
  60 PROCbasis
  70 END
  80
 500 DEF PROCinput
 510 INPUT "NUMBER OF MAIN +SLACK +SURPLUS VARIABLES ";N
 520 INPUT "NUMBER OF CONSTRAINTS ";M
 530 ENDPROC
 540
1000 DEF PROCbasis
1010 FOR j= 1 TO M
1020 K(j) = j
1030 NEXT j
1040 PROCprint
1050 REPEAT
1060 j=M+1
1070 REPEAT
1080 j=j-1
1090 UNTIL K(j) < N-M+j
1100 K(j) = K(j)+1
1110 FOR L = j+1 TO M
1120 K(L) = K(L-1)+1
1130 NEXT L
1140 PROCprint
1150 UNTIL K(1)=N-M+1
1160 ENDPROC
1170
1500 DEF PROCprint
1510 V = V+1
1520 PRINT "VERTEX ";STR$(V);
1530 FOR J = 1 TO M
1540 PRINT "  x";STR$(K(J));
1550 NEXT J
1560 PRINT
1570 ENDPROC
```

Of course, it is desirable to develop the program to evaluate the values of the variables and objective function for each candidate basis. This can be achieved by ignoring the non-basic variables and solving the resulting constraint equations. Program ENUMER below uses Gaussian elimination for this purpose but the details need not detain the reader (see *BASIC matrix methods* by J. Mason, Butterworths, 1984). Amend VERTEX as follows:

```
20 REM OBTAINS VARIABLE VALUES BY GAUSSIAN ELIMINATION

40 DIM K(10),a(10,10),b(10),c(10),A(10,10),B(10),C(10),X(10)

1040 PROCgauss

1140 PROCgauss
```

Now type in lines 530–650, DELETE lines 1500–1570, and type in lines 2000 *et seq.* from the listing of ENUMER below. The purpose of these PROCEDURES is described below.

PROCgauss:	controls Gaussian elimination in stages $K = 1, 2, \ldots, M-1$, and calls the following Procedures.
PROCdata:	sets up the M constraint equations without the non-basic variables in the form $Ax = C$ where A is the matrix of coefficients and C is the RHS vector.
PROCfind_pivot:	finds the largest entry in the Kth column $A(R,K) = MAX (A(I,K))$.
PROCinterchange_rows:	interchanges rows R and K when $R>K$, i.e. the largest entry in Kth col. is below the diagonal.
PROCelimination:	$A(I,K)$ is made zero by additions of the new Kth row for $I = K + 1, \ldots, M$.
PROCback_subst:	if $A(M,M) = 0$ the matrix is singular otherwise the x_j are determined successively for $j = M, M - 1, \ldots, 2,1$ and then z is evaluated.
PROCmat_print:	prints out the current A and C.

Program 6.2 ENUMER: Obtains values of basic variables for all bases

```
   5 REM ENUMER
  10 REM CANDIDATE BASIC VARIABLE SETS IN LEXICOGRAPHIC ORDER
  20 REM OBTAINS VARIABLE VALUES BY GAUSSIAN ELIMINATION
  30 @%=&020210
  40 DIM K(10),a(10,10),b(10),c(10),A(10,10),B(10),C(10),X(10)
  50 PROCinput
  60 PROCbasis
  70 END
  80
 500 DEF PROCinput
 510 INPUT "NUMBER OF MAIN +SLACK +SURPLUS VARIABLES ";N
 520 INPUT "NUMBER OF CONSTRAINTS ";M
 530 FOR I = 1 TO M
 540 PRINT "INPUT a(i,j) & c(i) for constraint i=";STR$(I)
 550 FOR J=1 TO N
 560 PRINT "a(";STR$(I);",";STR$(J);") = "; :INPUT a(I,J);
 570 NEXT J
 580 PRINT "c(";STR$(I);") = ";:INPUT c(I)
 590 NEXT I
 600 PRINT "Now input the obj. fn. coeffs. b(j) "
 610 FOR J= 1 TO N-M
 620 PRINT "b(";STR$(J);")=";:INPUT b(J);
 630 NEXT J
 640 ENDPROC
 650
1000 DEF PROCbasis
1010 FOR j= 1 TO M
1020 K(j) = j
1030 NEXT j
1040 PROCgauss
1050 REPEAT
1060 j=M+1
1070 REPEAT
1080 j=j-1
1090 UNTIL K(j) < N-M+j
1100 K(j) = K(j)+1
1110 FOR L = j+1 TO M
1120 K(L) = K(L-1)+1
1130 NEXT L
1140 PROCgauss
1150 UNTIL K(1)=N-M+1
1160 ENDPROC
1170
2000 DEF PROCgauss
2010 PROCdata
2020 FOR K= 1 TO M-1
2030 PROCfind_pivot
2040 IF R>K THEN PROCinterchange_rows
2050 PROCelimination
2060 NEXT K
2070 PROCback_subst
2080 PROCprint_basis
2090 ENDPROC
2100
3000 DEF PROCdata
3010 M$="NS"
3020 FOR I = 1 TO M
3030 C(I) = c(I)
3040 FOR J = 1 TO M
3050 A(I,J)=a(I,K(J))
3060 NEXT J
3070 NEXT I
3080 ENDPROC
3090
```

```
3500 DEF PROCfind_pivot
3510 D=0 : R=K
3520 FOR I = K TO M
3530 C = ABS(A(I,K))
3540 IF D < C THEN D=C : R=I
3550 NEXT I
3560 ENDPROC
3570
4000 DEF PROCinterchange_rows
4010 FOR J = K TO M
4020 D = A(K,J)
4030 A(K,J) = A(R,J)
4040 A(R,J) = D
4050 NEXT J
4060 D = C(K)
4070 C(K) = C(R)
4080 C(R) = D
4090 PROCmat_print
4100 ENDPROC
4110
4500 DEF PROCelimination
4510 FOR I = K+1 TO M
4520 D = -A(I,K)/A(K,K)
4530 FOR J = 1 TO M
4540 A(I,J) = A(I,J) + D*A(K,J)
4550 NEXT J
4560 C(I) = C(I) + D*C(K)
4570 NEXT I
4580 PROCmat_print
4590 ENDPROC
4600
5000 DEF PROCback_subst
5010 IF ABS(A(M,M))>0 THEN X(M)=C(M)/A(M,M) ELSE M$="S":ENDPROC
5020 Z = X(M)*b(K(M))
5030 FOR I = M-1 TO 1 STEP -1
5040 D=C(I)
5050 FOR J= I+1 TO M
5060 D=D-A(I,J)*X(J)
5070 NEXT J
5080 X(I) = D/A(I,I)
5090 Z = Z + X(I)*b(K(I))
5100 NEXT I
5110 ENDPROC
5120
5500 DEF PROCprint_basis
5510 V=V+1 : PRINT "VERTEX ";STR$(V);" ";
5520 FOR J = 1 TO M
5530 PRINT " x";STR$(K(J));
5540 IF M$<>"S" THEN PRINT "=";X(J);
5550 NEXT J
5560 IF M$<>"S" THEN PRINT " OBJ.FN.=";Z
5570 IF M$="S" THEN PRINT " SINGULAR MATRIX"
5580 PRINT
5590 ENDPROC
5600
6000 DEF PROCmat_print
6010 FOR I= 1 TO M
6020 FOR J= 1 TO M
6030 PRINT " ";A(I,J);
6040 NEXT J
6050 PRINT " ";C(I)
6060 NEXT I
6070 PRINT
6080 ENDPROC
```

RUN this program in Mode 3 for the data of problem P2, noting
that it is again necessary to input the matrix of constraint
coefficients after the addition of slack and surplus variables. The
printout gives the matrix of coefficients of the constraints
following each stage of Gaussian elimination. When you
understand how this works you can DELETE lines numbered
4090, 4580 and 5580. The vertex numbering conforms to that in
Figure 6.4. You should note in particular that vertices 3, 12 and 13
are coincident, which is because three rather than two constraint
boundaries define this (infeasible) vertex. A basis corresponding
to a vertex of this kind is said to be degenerate, since one of the
basic variables would actually be zero. Do Problem 6.1 at this
stage.

```
RUN
NUMBER OF MAIN +SLACK +SURPLUS VARIABLES ?6
NUMBER OF CONSTRAINTS ?4
INPUT a(i,j) & c(i) for constraint i=1
a(1,1) = ?2
a(1,2) = ?1
a(1,3) = ?1
a(1,4) = ?0
a(1,5) = ?0
a(1,6) = ?0
c(1) = ?500
INPUT a(i,j) & c(i) for constraint i=2
a(2,1) = ?0
a(2,2) = ?1
a(2,3) = ?0
a(2,4) = ?1
a(2,5) = ?0
a(2,6) = ?0
c(2) = ?200
INPUT a(i,j) & c(i) for constraint i=3
a(3,1) = ?1
a(3,2) = ?2
a(3,3) = ?0
a(3,4) = ?0
a(3,5) = ?-1
a(3,6) = ?0
c(3) = ?400
INPUT a(i,j) & c(i) for constraint i=4
a(4,1) = ?1
a(4,2) = ?0
a(4,3) = ?0
a(4,4) = ?0
a(4,5) = ?0
a(4,6) = ?-1
c(4) = ?100
Now input the obj. fn. coeffs. b(j)
b(1)=?3
b(2)=?1
VERTEX 1   x1=100.00 x2=150.00 x3=150.00 x4=50.00 OBJ.FN.=450.00
VERTEX 2   x1=100.00 x2=200.00 x3=100.00 x5=100.00 OBJ.FN.=500.00
VERTEX 3   x1=0.00 x2=200.00 x3=300.00 x6=-100.00 OBJ.FN.=200.00
```

```
VERTEX  4   x1=100.00  x2=300.00  x4=-100.00  x5=300.00  OBJ.FN.=600.00
VERTEX  5   x1=200.00  x2=100.00  x4=100.00  x6=100.00  OBJ.FN.=700.00
VERTEX  6   x1=150.00  x2=200.00  x5=150.00  x6=50.00  OBJ.FN.=650.00
VERTEX  7   x1=100.00  x3=300.00  x4=200.00  x5=-300.00  OBJ.FN.=300.00
VERTEX  8   x1=400.00  x3=-300.00  x4=200.00  x6=300.00  OBJ.FN.=1200.00
VERTEX  9   x1  x3  x5  x6  SINGULAR MATRIX
VERTEX 10   x1=250.00  x4=200.00  x5=-150.00  x6=150.00  OBJ.FN.=750.00
VERTEX 11   x2  x3  x4  x5  SINGULAR MATRIX
VERTEX 12   x2=200.00  x3=300.00  x4=0.00  x6=-100.00  OBJ.FN.=200.00
VERTEX 13   x2=200.00  x3=300.00  x5=0.00  x6=-100.00  OBJ.FN.=200.00
VERTEX 14   x2=500.00  x4=-300.00  x5=600.00  x6=-100.00  OBJ.FN.=500.00
VERTEX 15   x3=500.00  x4=200.00  x5=-400.00  x6=-100.00  OBJ.FN.=0.00
```

6.2 The simplex method of linear programming

The reader will have been struck by the very considerable amount of calculation involved in the process of enumerating the objective function at each vertex. The situation would be improved somewhat if some way could be found of concentrating on the enumeration of feasible vertices. Indeed, it is fairly obvious that in principle a 'Cook's Tour' could be made of the vertices which define the extreme points of the feasible region. Pairs of feasible vertices are adjacent in the sense that a line segment of the constraint boundary connects them. So the corresponding non-basic variable is held in common, and indeed adjacent feasible vertices have bases which differ in respect of a single variable. This observation provides both the means to carry out a 'Cook's Tour' and a method for deriving one adjacent basis from another with comparatively little computation.

It is vital to appreciate that if a feasible vertex can be found with a better objective function value than any of the adjacent feasible vertices, then it provides an optimum solution. A local optimum in linear programming is a global optimum. This desirable property has been established by mathematicians whatever the number of variables and constraints may be. This property provides the key to a scheme of partial vertex enumeration which terminates with the optimum solution, just as soon as adjacent vertices fail to yield an improvement upon the current objective function value. Thus the idea underlying the simplex method is to start from an initial feasible vertex and to move along a constraint boundary to an adjacent vertex, terminating with a local optimum. This is a process of partial enumeration of feasible vertices, which can be implemented via basic feasible solutions.

Take the former problem P1 which was restated as

$$\text{Maximise } z = 3x_1 + x_2$$
$$2x_1 + x_2 + x_3 \qquad = 500$$
$$x_2 \qquad + x_4 = 200$$
$$x_1, x_2 \qquad \geqslant 0$$

An obvious initial basis for problem P1 is at the origin where the slacks take the right-hand side values of the constraints, i.e. the enumeration begins with vertex f of Figure 6.3. The objective function can now be rewritten in the same format as the constraints, as shown below in a *simplex tableau*. Notice that the non-basic variables (numerically zero) at this stage are easily distinguishable from the basic variables. Each basic variable has an empty column of coefficients save for the unit entry in the basic variable row, i.e. a unit column vector.

Basic	z	x_1	x_2	x_3	x_4	RHS	Ratio
z	1	-3	-1	0	0	0	N/A
$*x_3$	0	$2*$	1	1	0	500	250
x_4	0	0	1	0	1	200	Infinite
		$*$					

Consequently an increase in either x_1 or x_2 increases the numerical value of z because of the negative z row coefficients in the x_1 and x_2 columns. If x_1 increases on its own then the boundary of the feasible region is traversed from the initial vertex f toward vertex c. An increase in x_2 begins a traversal of the boundary from vertex f toward vertex d. This can be seen from Figure 6.3 (page 85).

The z row coefficients represent the negative rates of change of z with increases in the non-basic variables x_1 and x_2. A rule of thumb is to choose to increase that non-basic variable which confers the fastest rate of improvement in z, x_1 in this case. Bringing x_1 into the basis in this way is recorded by the asterisk at the foot of the x_1 column of the tableau, which is now referred to as the *pivot column*.

There is a limitation upon possible increases in the value of x_1, however, since traversal of the constraint boundary from vertex f must halt at vertex c if feasibility is to be retained. This vertex is defined by the constraint boundary $x_3 = 0$, and so the variable x_3 which was a basic variable at vertex f becomes a non-basic variable at vertex c. All this can be directly inferred from the simplex tableau, by forming the ratio of the RHS value to the pivot column entry for each constraint. The ratio gives the increase in the new basic variable which results from driving the old basic variable to zero, and therefore out of the new basis. In the case of the tableau above the value of the ratio in the x_3 row shows that x_1 reaches 250 as x_3 becomes zero. Since the ratio is infinitely large in the case of the final constraint x_1 can approach infinity without driving x_4 to zero. The permissible increase in x_1 is then the minimum of the ratios, and the corresponding row is indicated by an asterisk and referred to as the *pivot row*.

It is important to realize that a negative pivot column entry means that the existing basic variable increases with the incoming basic variable in order to maintain an equality. This obviously places no restriction whatsoever upon the value of the new basic variable, and so an infinitely large ratio can be associated with a negative pivot column entry and likewise for a zero entry.

The *pivot* lies at the intersection of the pivot row and pivot column and is indicated by an asterisk. If the pivot row is divided by the pivot then a new row appears as follows, with the basic label changed to x_1:

Basic	z	x_1	x_2	x_3	x_4	RHS
z						
x_1	0	1	0.5	0.5	0	250
x_4						

This row can now be used to eliminate x_1 from the remaining rows. Thus adding thrice the new row to the z row and zero times the new row to the x_4 row gives the next simplex tableau.

Basic	z	x_1	x_2	x_3	x_4	RHS
z	1	0	0.5	1.5	0	750
x_1	0	1	0.5	0.5	0	250
x_4	0	0	1	0	1	200

The values of the new variables are seen to be $x_1 = 250$ and $x_4 = 200$, with x_2 and x_3 zero-valued, or non-basic variables. The objective function has the value 750. This is implicitly a maximum value, since the fact that all the z row coefficients of the non-basic variables are positive removes any scope for further improvement. This basis is associated with vertex c.

For problem P1, therefore, the simplex method has explicitly considered only the vertices f and c of the four vertices at the extreme points of the feasible region., Furthermore, the computational burden in the iteration which transformed the initial tableau to the final tableau was broadly equivalent to just the computations involved in the first stage of Gaussian elimination (i.e. when K = 1). So in this instance the partial enumeration of the feasible vertices was both effectively and efficiently conducted.

A listing of Program SIMPLEX follows. A main program calls

PROCinput: allows the user to input the matrix of coefficients $A(I, J)$ of the main variables x_J and the non-negative RHS values $C(I)$ in

	constraints $I = 1,2,\ldots M$. The objective function coefficients $C(J)$ are input and copied into $A(0, J)$.
PROCprint:	initially prints out the data as input when EDIT=1, then prints the entire simplex tableau less the z column. The signature of z is $-$ for minimization.
PROCslacks:	slacks with indices $N+I$ are added to the constraints for $I = 1,2,\ldots,M$, and are then made basic, which is recorded by setting $STATUS(N+I) = 1$ and $A(I, 0) = N+I$.
PROCiterate:	controls iterations via the following:
PROCpivot_column:	seeks most negative $A(0, J)$ to identify the pivot column j, ignoring spurious $A(0, J) > -E-08$. Sets $STATUS(j) = 1$.
PROCpivot_row:	seeks row i with smallest non-negative ratio of RHS/pivot column entry, and sets $STATUS(A(i, 0)) = 0$.
PROCpivot:	records $A(i, 0) = j$ and uses the pivot row to eliminate x_j from all other rows.

Now type in the program SIMPLEX from the following listing.

Program 6.3 SIMPLEX: LP for <= constraints with non-negative RHS

```
   5 REM SIMPLEX
  10 REM M <= INEQUALITIES WITH NON-NEGATIVE R.H.S.
  20 REM N DECISION VARIABLES AND M INEQUALITIES s.t. N+M<21
  30 REM USES SLACK VARIABLES FOR IFS
  40 @%=&020310
  50 DIM A(11,21),B(21),C(11),STATUS(21)
  60 ITERATION=0
  70 PROCinput
  80 PROCprint
  90 EDIT=0
 100 PROCslacks
 110 N=N+M
 120 PRINT : PRINT "PRIMAL FEASIBLE TABLEAU" : PROCprint
 130 PROCiterate
 140 END
 150
 500 DEF PROCinput
 510 INPUT "number of main variables ",N
 520 INPUT "number of <= constraints ",M
 530 PRINT
 540 FOR I= 1 TO M
 550 PRINT "input a(i,j) & c(i) for constraint i=";STR$(I)
 560 FOR J= 1 TO N
 570 PRINT "a(";STR$(I);",";STR$(J);")=";:INPUT A(I,J)
 580 NEXT J
 590 PRINT "c(";STR$(I);")=";:INPUT C(I)
 600 NEXT I
 610 INPUT "type of objective function (enter MAX or MIN)",Z$
 620 PRINT "Now input the objective function coeffs b(j)"
 630 FOR J=1 TO N
 640 PRINT "b(";STR$(J);")=";:INPUT B(J);
 650 IF Z$ = "MIN" THEN A(0,J)=B(J)
 660 IF Z$ = "MAX" THEN A(0,J)=-B(J)
 670 NEXT J
 680 EDIT =1
 690 PRINT : PRINT "ROWS AS INPUT"
 700 ENDPROC
 710
1000 DEF PROCprint
1010 PRINT :IF EDIT=0 THEN PRINT "BASIC";ELSE PRINT "TYPE";
1020 FOR J = 1 TO N
1030 PRINT TAB(10*J);"X";STR$(J);
1040 NEXT J
1050 PRINT TAB(10*(N+1));"R.H.S."
1060 PRINT
1070 FOR I= 0 TO M
1080 FOR J= 0 TO N
1090 IF Z$="MAX" AND I=0 AND J=0 THEN PRINT "Z";
1100 IF Z$="MIN" AND I=0 AND J=0 THEN PRINT "-Z";
1110 IF EDIT=0 AND I>0 AND J=0 THEN PRINT "X";STR$(A(I,0));
1120 IF EDIT=1 AND I>0 AND J=0 THEN PRINT "L";
1130 IF J>0 THEN PRINT TAB(10*J);A(I,J);
1140 NEXT J
1150 PRINT TAB((N+1)*10);C(I)
1160 NEXT I
1170 PRINT
1180 ENDPROC
1190
2500 DEF PROCslacks
2510 FOR I= 1 TO M
2520 A(I,0) = N+I
2530 A(I,N+I) = 1
2540 STATUS(N+I) = 1
2550 NEXT I
2560 ENDPROC
2570
```

```
4500 DEF PROCiterate
4510 REPEAT
4520 PROCpivot_column
4530 IF j=0 THEN ENDPROC
4550 PROCpivot_row
4560 IF i=0 THEN PRINT "UNBOUNDED SOLN":END
4570 p = A(i,j)
4580 PRINT "PIVOT =";p;"  NEW BASIC VAR. X";STR$(j);
4590 PRINT " IN PLACE OF X";STR$(A(i,0))
4600 PROCpivot
4620 PRINT : PRINT "ITERATION No ";STR$(ITERATION)
4630 PROCprint
4640 UNTIL FALSE
4650 ENDPROC
4660
5000 DEF PROCpivot_column
5010 BEST = 0 : COEFF = 0 : j = 0
5020 FOR J= 1 TO N
5030 IF A(0,J) < - 1E-08 THEN COEFF = -A(0,J)
5050 IF COEFF > BEST THEN BEST = COEFF : j = J
5060 NEXT J
5070 STATUS(j) = 1
5080 ENDPROC
5090
5500 DEF PROCpivot_row
5510 RATIO = 10E10 : TEST = 10E10 : i = 0
5520 FOR I= 1 TO M
5530 IF A(I,j) > 1E-08 THEN TEST = C(I)/A(I,j)
5540 IF TEST < RATIO THEN RATIO = TEST : i = I
5550 NEXT I
5560 STATUS(A(i,0)) = 0
5570 ENDPROC
5580
6000 DEF PROCpivot
6010 A(i,0) = j
6020 REM DIVIDE PIVOT ROW BY PIVOT
6030 FOR J = 1 TO N
6040 A(i,J) = A(i,J)/p
6050 NEXT J
6060 C(i)=C(i)/p :REM STORE OLD PIVOT COLUMN ENTRY IN COL
6070 FOR I = 0 TO M
6080 COL = A(I,j)
6090 FOR J= 1 TO N
6100 IF I <>i THEN A(I,J) = A(I,J)-COL*A(i,J)
6110 NEXT J
6120 IF I <> i THEN C(I) = C(I)-COL*C(i)
6130 NEXT I
6140 ITERATION = ITERATION + 1
6150 ENDPROC
6160


>RUN
number of main variables ?2
number of <= constraints ?2

input a(i,j) & c(i) for constraint i=1
a(1,1)=?2
a(1,2)=?1
c(1)=?500
input a(i,j) & c(i) for constraint i=2
a(2,1)=?0
a(2,2)=?1
c(2)=?200
type of objective function (enter MAX or MIN)?MAX
Now input the objective function coeffs b(j)
b(1)=?3
b(2)=?1
```

```
ROWS AS INPUT

TYPE    X1      X2      R.H.S.


Z       -3.000  -1.000  0.000
L        2.000   1.000  500.000
L        0.000   1.000  200.000



PRIMAL FEASIBLE TABLEAU


BASIC   X1      X2      X3      X4      R.H.S.


Z       -3.000  -1.000  0.000   0.000   0.000
X3       2.000   1.000  1.000   0.000   500.000
X4       0.000   1.000  0.000   1.000   200.000

PIVOT =2.000  NEW BASIC VAR. X1 IN PLACE OF X3

ITERATION No 1

BASIC   X1      X2      X3      X4      R.H.S.


Z        0.000   0.500  1.500   0.000   750.000
X1       1.000   0.500  0.500   0.000   250.000
X4       0.000   1.000  0.000   1.000   200.000
```

When satisfied with the accuracy of your listing you should
RUN with the data of problem P1, noting that it is only necessary
to input the matrix of coefficients of main variables, as the slack
variables are entered automatically by the program. Your printout
should agree with the sequence of tableaux described earlier,
except that the z column is omitted as it does not change. You
should do Problems 6.2 to 6.5 now.

It is computationally convenient to transform minimization
objective functions into equivalent maximization functions with

$$\text{MIN } z = -\text{MAX } -z$$
$$\text{or} \quad \text{MIN } \quad b_1 x_1 + b_2 x_2 + \ldots + b_n x_n$$
$$= -\text{MAX } -b_1 x_1 - b_2 x_2 - \ldots - b_n x_n$$

For instance, you should check that this transformation holds for
P1 by RUNning SIMPLEX with the minimization objective

$$-\text{MIN } -3x_1 - x_2$$

If the search for the pivot row is frustrated by a pivot column of
negative elements then there is no restriction upon the value of the
incoming basic variable. In short, the solution is unbounded due to
a shortcoming in the formulation of the problem (see line 4560).

The simplex method implicitly assumes an improvement in the
value of the objective function at each iteration, since only then

can one be sure of termination with the optimun solution in a finite number of iterations. A degenerate basis is one in which one or more basic variables happens to be zero, and this can occur if more than n constraints intersect at a vertex. But if the pivot row happens to have the zero right-hand side value in a degenerate basis then the value of z remains unchanged in the next tableau. This opens up the possibility of an endless 'cycling' of iterations around a subset of the vertices, without ever reaching an optimum. This is unlikely to occur in practice, but one of the problems is to RUN a specially constructed problem with several degenerate bases which does, in fact, cycle.

Program SIMPLEX will fail to recognize the existence of an alternative optimum, which arises when a non-basic variable j has a zero-valued z coefficient $A(0, j)$. Amendments to the program are left to the interested reader, who should do Problems 6.6 to 6.7 at this juncture.

6.3 Mixed inequality and equality constraints

The slack variables were used as an initial basis in SIMPLEX. But this approach cannot be employed for surplus variables which are subtracted from the left-hand side of $>=$ constraints with non-negative RHS, since a feasible basis must have non-negative variables throughout. Take problem P2 as an illustration; one could not have $x_5 = -400$ and $x_6 = -100$ here

$$
\begin{aligned}
\text{MAX } z = 3x_1 + x_2 \\
2x_1 + x_2 + x_3 \qquad\qquad = 500 \\
x_2 \quad + x_4 \qquad = 200 \\
x_1 + 2x_2 \qquad - x_5 \qquad = 400 \\
x_1 \qquad\qquad - x_6 = 100
\end{aligned}
$$

Another transformation can be used to overcome this difficulty with the $>=$ constraints. First identify the $>=$ constraint, I0 say, with the largest right-hand side. Next substitute for the other $>=$ constraints, in turn, the results of subtracting them from the I0 constraint. In this case I0=3 and so row 4 is replaced by row 3 minus row 4.

$$
\begin{aligned}
\text{MAX } z = 3x_1 + x_2 \\
2x_1 + x_2 + x_3 \qquad\qquad = 500 \\
x_2 \quad + x_4 \qquad = 200 \\
x_1 + 2x_2 \qquad - x_5 \qquad = 400 \\
2x_2 \qquad - x_5 + x_6 = 300
\end{aligned}
$$

This transformation reverses the sign of the surplus variable in each $>=$ constraint, save the I0 constraint, whilst preserving a non-negative right-hand side. As a result these surplus variables are now obvious basis candidates, and $x_6=300$ is a basic variable in this example. But the I0 constraint still poses a real problem, and so an *artifical* variable x_7 is introduced into the left-hand side.

$$x_1 + 2x_2 \qquad\qquad - x_5 + x_7 = 400$$

The artificial is made basic, thus $x_7 = 400$ here. This completes an initial basis to the wrong problem! If we chose to minimize x_7 as a first objective, then immediately x_7 was driven to zero we would have an initial basis to the original problem P2. The original objective could then be taken up and the iterations pursued to optimality.

In summary, an artifical variable x_7 is introduced into the I0 constraint and made basic; the objective is to minimize x_7 in Phase 1, and when this is achieved the original objective is reinstated in Phase 0. The following details are implicit. The z row is transformed during Phase 1 as if it were a constraint row, in order to express it in terms of the current non-basic variables, and at the start of Phase 1 the objective function x_0, say, must also be written in terms of non-basic variables.

$$\text{MIN } x_0 = x_7 = -x_1 - 2x_2 + x_5 + 400$$

The same broad approach can be developed to cater for equality constraints as well. An artificial variable is assigned to each equality constraint, and the phase 1 objective is the minimization of the sum of artificals.

If there are E equality constraints, L $<=$ constraints, G $>=$ constraints then there will be A=E+1 artificial variables (or A=E if G=0). It is convenient to have PROCinput sort the input data so as to place the equality constraints in the last E rows. Each row I then has an extra variable x_{N+I} which is either a slack added to $<=$ constraints, a surplus subtracted from $>=$ constraints, or an artificial added to = constraints. If G>0 there will also be an artificial x_{N+M+1} associated with row I0.

Program SIMPLEX can be developed to work in this way and Program 2PHASE, as it is called, involves the following changes and additions:

PROCinput: now allows the user to input the type of constraint, and counts L, G, E. Identifies I0 when G>0 and sorts the equalities into rows M, M−1, M−2, etc

PROCmatrix: sets up the matrix of coefficients A(I,J). Calls PROCslacks if L>0, PROCartificial and

	PROCtransform if G>0, PROCequalities if E>0. Lists the artificials when A>0.
PROCartificial:	adds an artificial to the I0 row and makes it basic, increments the x_0 coeffs by the I0 row coefficients.
PROCtransform:	carries out the transformations on the >= inequalities, making surpluses basic.
PROCequalities:	increments the x_0 coeffs by the E row coefficients, making artificials basic.
PROCphase:	sets PHASE = 1 for first phase, PHASE = 0 for second phase when all artificials have been driven from the basis.

Load SIMPLEX and make the following alterations and additions, as found in the listing of 2PHASE below.

Amend lines: 5   520   541–547   570–572   590–595
                1070   1120   4530–4540   4610   5030–5040
                6070
Delete lines: 2510   2550
Type in: Main program   PROCmatrix   PROCartificial
            PROCtransform   PROCequalities   PROCphase

Now check your listing against the listing for 2PHASE below.

Program 6.4 2PHASE: LP for mixed inequality and equality constraints with non-negative RHS

```
   5 REM 2PHASE
  10 REM M<11 INEQUALITIES PLUS EQUATIONS WITH NON-NEG RHS
  20 REM WITH N DECISION VARIABLES LIMITS ARE N+M<21
  30 REM USES 2-PHASE METHOD WITH ARTIFICIAL VARIABLES
  40 @%=&020310
  50 DIM A(11,21),B(21),C(11),STATUS(21),TYPE$(11)
  60 ITERATION=0 :L=0 :E=0 :G=0 :PHASE=0 :A=0 :CMAX=0 :I0=0
  70 PROCinput
  80 PROCprint
  90 EDIT=0
 100 PROCmatrix
 110 PROCprint
 120 PROCiterate
 130 END
 140
 500 DEF PROCinput
 510 INPUT "number of main variables ",N
 520 INPUT "number of constraints ",M
 530 PRINT
 540 FOR I= 1 TO M
 541 PRINT
 542 PRINT "input type of constraint i=";STR$(I)
 543 PRINT "i.e. input L ,E ,G for <= ,= ,>= " ;
 544 INPUT TYPE$
 545 IF TYPE$="L" THEN L=L+1 : TYPE$(I-E)="L"
 546 IF TYPE$="G" THEN G=G+1 : TYPE$(I-E)="G"
 547 IF TYPE$="E" THEN E=E+1 : TYPE$(M-E+1)="E"
 550 PRINT "input a(i,j) & c(i) for constraint i=";STR$(I)
 560 FOR J= 1 TO N
 570 PRINT "a(";STR$(I);",";STR$(J);")=";
 571 IF TYPE$= "E" THEN INPUT TAB(10) A(M-E+1,J)
 572 IF TYPE$<>"E" THEN INPUT TAB(10) A(I-E,J)
 580 NEXT J
 590 PRINT "c(";STR$(I);")=";
 591 IF TYPE$= "E" THEN INPUT TAB(10) C(M-E+1)
 592 IF TYPE$<>"E" THEN INPUT TAB(10) C(I-E)
 595 IF TYPE$="G" AND C(I-E)>=CMAX THEN CMAX=C(I-E) :I0=I-E
 600 NEXT I
 610 INPUT "type of objective function (enter MAX or MIN)",Z$
 620 PRINT "Now input the objective function coeffs b(j)"
 630 FOR J=1 TO N
 640 PRINT "b(";STR$(J);")=";:INPUT B(J);
 650 IF Z$ = "MIN" THEN A(0,J) = B(J)
 660 IF Z$ = "MAX" THEN A(0,J) = -B(J)
 670 NEXT J
 680 EDIT =1
 690 PRINT : PRINT "ROWS AS INPUT"
 700 ENDPROC
 710
1000 DEF PROCprint
1010 PRINT : IF EDIT=0 THEN PRINT "BASIC";ELSE PRINT "TYPE";
1020 FOR J = 1 TO N
1030 PRINT TAB(10*J);"X";STR$(J);
1040 NEXT J
1050 PRINT TAB(10*(N+1));"R.H.S."
1060 PRINT
1070 FOR I= 0 TO M+PHASE
1080 FOR J=0 TO N
1090 IF Z$="MAX" AND I=0 AND J=0 THEN PRINT "Z";
1100 IF Z$="MIN" AND I=0 AND J=0 THEN PRINT "-Z";
1110 IF EDIT=0 AND I>0 AND J=0 THEN PRINT "X";STR$(A(I,0));
1120 IF EDIT=1 AND I>0 AND J=0 THEN PRINT TYPE$(I);
1130 IF J>0 THEN PRINT TAB(10*J);A(I,J);
1140 NEXT J
1150 PRINT TAB((N+1)*10);C(I)
1160 NEXT I
1170 PRINT
1180 ENDPROC
1190
```

```
2000 DEF PROCmatrix
2010 IF G>0 THEN PROCartificial
2020 FOR I=1 TO M-E
2030 IF TYPE$(I) = "L" THEN PROCslacks
2040 IF TYPE$(I) = "G" AND I<>I0 THEN PROCtransform
2050 NEXT I
2060 IF E>0 THEN PROCequalities
2070 IF E+G > 0 THEN PHASE = 1
2080 IF G>0 THEN A=1
2090 A = A+E : PRINT
2100 IF A>0 THEN PRINT "ARTIFICIAL VARIABLES REQUIRED"
2110 IF E>0 THEN FOR I=M-E+1 TO M:PRINT "X";STR$(N+I):NEXT I
2120 IF G>0 THEN PRINT "X";STR$(N+M+1)
2130 IF G>0 THEN N=N+M+1 ELSE N=N+M
2140 PRINT : PRINT "PRIMAL FEASIBLE TABLEAU"
2150 ENDPROC
2160
2500 DEF PROCslacks
2520 A(I,0) = N+I
2530 A(I,N+I) = 1
2540 STATUS(N+I)=1
2560 ENDPROC
2570
3000 DEF PROCartificial
3010 A(I0,N+I0) = -1
3020 A(I0,0) = N+M+1
3030 A(I0,N+M+1) = 1
3040 STATUS(N+M+1) = 1
3050 FOR J = 1 TO N+M
3060 A(M+1,J) = A(M+1,J) + A(I0,J)
3070 NEXT J
3080 C(M+1) = C(M+1) + C(I0)
3090 ENDPROC
3100
3500 DEF PROCtransform
3510 FOR J = 1 TO N+M-E
3520 A(I,J)=A(I0,J)-A(I,J)
3530 NEXT J
3540 C(I)=C(I0)-C(I)
3550 A(I,0)=N+I
3560 A(I,N+I)=1
3570 STATUS(N+I)=1
3580 ENDPROC
3590
4000 DEF PROCequalities
4010 FOR I = M-E+1 TO M
4020 FOR J = 1 TO N
4030 A(M+1,J) = A(M+1,J) + A(I,J)
4040 NEXT J
4050 C(M+1) = C(M+1) + C(I)
4060 A(I,N+I)=1
4070 A(I,0)=N+I
4080 STATUS(N+I)=1
4090 NEXT I
4100 ENDPROC
4110
4500 DEF PROCiterate
4510 REPEAT
4520 PROCpivot_column
4530 IF j=0 AND PHASE=1 THEN PRINT "NO FEASIBLE BASIS" : END
4540 IF j=0 AND PHASE=0 THEN ENDPROC
4550 PROCpivot_row
4560 IF i=0 THEN PRINT "UNBOUNDED SOLN":END
4570 p = A(i,j)
4580 PRINT "PIVOT =";p;" NEW BASIC VAR. X";STR$(j);
4590 PRINT " IN PLACE OF X";STR$(A(i,0))
4600 PROCpivot
4610 IF PHASE=1 THEN PROCphase
4620 PRINT : PRINT "ITERATION No ";STR$(ITERATION)
4630 PROCprint
4640 UNTIL FALSE
4650 ENDPROC
4660
```

```
5000 DEF PROCpivot_column
5010 BEST = 0 : COEFF = 0 : j = 0
5020 FOR J= 1 TO N
5030 IF PHASE=0 AND A(0,J) < - 1E-08 THEN COEFF = -A(0,J)
5040 IF PHASE=1 AND A(M+1,J) > 1E-08 THEN COEFF = A(M+1,J)
5050 IF COEFF > BEST THEN BEST = COEFF : j = J
5060 NEXT J
5070 STATUS(j) = 1
5080 ENDPROC
5090
5500 DEF PROCpivot_row
5510 RATIO = 10E10 : TEST = 10E10 : i = 0
5520 FOR I= 1 TO M
5530 IF A(I,j) > 1E-08 THEN TEST = C(I)/A(I,j)
5540 IF TEST < RATIO THEN RATIO = TEST : i = I
5550 NEXT I
5560 STATUS(A(i,0)) = 0
5570 ENDPROC
5580
6000 DEF PROCpivot
6010 A(i,0) = j
6020 REM DIVIDE PIVOT ROW BY PIVOT
6030 FOR J = 1 TO N
6040 A(i,J) = A(i,J)/p
6050 NEXT J
6060 C(i)=C(i)/p :REM STORE OLD PIVOT COLUMN ENTRY IN COL
6070 FOR I = 0 TO M+PHASE
6080 COL = A(I,j)
6090 FOR J= 1 TO N
6100 IF I <>i THEN A(I,J) = A(I,J)-COL*A(i,J)
6110 NEXT J
6120 IF I <> i THEN C(I) = C(I)-COL*C(i)
6130 NEXT I
6140 ITERATION = ITERATION + 1
6150 ENDPROC
6160
6500 DEF PROCphase
6510 PHASE=0
6520 FOR I=N-A+1 TO N
6530 IF STATUS(I)=1 THEN PHASE=1
6540 NEXT I
6550 IF PHASE=0 THEN N=N-A
6560 ENDPROC
6570
```

Now RUN 2PHASE in Mode 3 for the data of problem P2, as overleaf. The output is readable, but not as clearly organized on a monitor as it is on a wide-carriage printer running in condensed font. Try Problems 6.8 to 6.11 here.

```
>RUN
number of main variables ?2
number of constraints ?4


input type of constraint i=1
i.e. input L ,E ,G for <= ,= ,)= ?L
input a(i,j) & c(i) for constraint i=1
a(1,1)=  2
a(1,2)=  1
c(1)=   500

input type of constraint i=2
i.e. input L ,E ,G for <= ,= ,)= ?L
input a(i,j) & c(i) for constraint i=2
a(2,1)=  0
a(2,2)=  1
c(2)=   200
```

```
input type of constraint i=3
i.e. input L ,E ,G for <= ,= ,)= ?G
input a(i,j) & c(i) for constraint i=3
a(3,1)=   1
a(3,2)=   2
c(3)=    400

input type of constraint i=4
i.e. input L ,E ,G for <= ,= ,)= ?G
input a(i,j) & c(i) for constraint i=4
a(4,1)=   1
a(4,2)=   0
c(4)=    100
type of objective function (enter MAX or MIN)?MAX
Now input the objective function coeffs b(j)
b(1)=?3
b(2)=?1
```

ROWS AS INPUT

TYPE	X1	X2	R.H.S.
Z	-3.000	-1.000	0.000
L	2.000	1.000	500.000
L	0.000	1.000	200.000
G	1.000	2.000	400.000
G	1.000	0.000	100.000

ARTIFICIAL VARIABLES REQUIRED
X7

PRIMAL FEASIBLE TABLEAU

BASIC	X1	X2	X3	X4	X5	X6	X7	R.H.S.
Z	-3.000	-1.000	0.000	0.000	0.000	0.000	0.000	0.000
X3	2.000	1.000	1.000	0.000	0.000	0.000	0.000	500.000
X4	0.000	1.000	0.000	1.000	0.000	0.000	0.000	200.000
X7	1.000	2.000	0.000	0.000	-1.000	0.000	1.000	400.000
X6	0.000	2.000	0.000	0.000	-1.000	1.000	0.000	300.000
X0	1.000	2.000	0.000	0.000	-1.000	0.000	0.000	400.000

PIVOT =2.000   NEW BASIC VAR. X2 IN PLACE OF X6

ITERATION No 1

BASIC	X1	X2	X3	X4	X5	X6	X7	R.H.S.
Z	-3.000	0.000	0.000	0.000	-0.500	0.500	0.000	150.000
X3	2.000	0.000	1.000	0.000	0.500	-0.500	0.000	350.000
X4	0.000	0.000	0.000	1.000	0.500	-0.500	0.000	50.000
X7	1.000	0.000	0.000	0.000	0.000	-1.000	1.000	100.000
X2	0.000	1.000	0.000	0.000	-0.500	0.500	0.000	150.000
X0	1.000	0.000	0.000	0.000	0.000	-1.000	0.000	100.000

PIVOT =1.000   NEW BASIC VAR. X1 IN PLACE OF X7

ITERATION No 2

BASIC	X1	X2	X3	X4	X5	X6	R.H.S.
Z	0.000	0.000	0.000	0.000	-0.500	-2.500	450.000
X3	0.000	0.000	1.000	0.000	0.500	1.500	150.000
X4	0.000	0.000	0.000	1.000	0.500	-0.500	50.000
X1	1.000	0.000	0.000	0.000	0.000	-1.000	100.000
X2	0.000	1.000	0.000	0.000	-0.500	0.500	150.000

PIVOT =1.500 NEW BASIC VAR. X6 IN PLACE OF X3

ITERATION No 3

BASIC	X1	X2	X3	X4	X5	X6	R.H.S.
Z	0.000	0.000	1.667	0.000	0.333	0.000	700.000
X6	0.000	0.000	0.667	0.000	0.333	1.000	100.000
X4	0.000	0.000	0.333	1.000	0.667	0.000	100.000
X1	1.000	0.000	0.667	0.000	0.333	0.000	200.000
X2	0.000	1.000	-0.333	0.000	-0.667	0.000	100.000

6.4 Post-optimal analysis

So far we have used only the information in the 'Basic' column and the 'RHS' column of the final tableau. The rest of the tableau contains information of considerable value in *post-optimal analysis*. The details are somewhat involved, and the reader may consult references 2 and 4 in Chapter 2 for authoritative accounts. A brief description of the main points of post-optimal analysis is provided here for those interested. Others may go straight on to the listing of the extra Procedures below.

Consider the inequality constraints. If a particular 'slack' ('surplus') variable x is basic then the constraint is loose, and the RHS value can be reduced (increased) by the value of the variable, and increased (reduced) without bound. A non-basic 'slack' ('surplus') variable x results from a *binding* constraint. A unit relaxation in the RHS value will result in a change in the values of the basic variables, and an improved objective function value. The correspondence works as follows. The coefficients in the x column in the final tableau must have been a result of elementary row operations on the constraint in question. Thus a unit relaxation in the original RHS would change the RHS column in the final tableau by the absolute magnitude of the x column coefficients. This must mean that the objective function value changes by the entry in the z row of the x column. Economists call this the 'shadow price' of a scarce unit of resource. The same rationale allows the calculation of the extent of permissible changes to the original RHS values which would leave the current basic variables non-negative, and this is known as *RHS* ranging.

Consider next the main variables. If a main variable x is non-basic then a sufficiently favourable change in the original objective function coefficient would lead to a zero x coefficient in the z row of the final tableau. The maximum change allowable, if x is to remain non-basic, is given by the x coefficient in the z row of the optimum tableau. On the other hand, there is no restriction upon unfavourable change in the original objective function coefficient of x. If a main variable is basic, then there are likely to be restrictions on increases and decreases in the original objective function coefficient of x, given that the final basis is to remain optimal. The effect on z of a unit increase (decrease) in the coefficient of x is simply to add (subtract) the x row to (from) the z row in the final tableau. The resulting z coefficients must remain non-negative if the final tableau is to remain optimal. One can thus determine maximal decreases and increases in the original x coefficient which preserve optimality; this is known as *ranging of the objective function coefficients*.

SENSITY is a development of 2PHASE which involves two PROCEDURES as follows.

PROCrhs_ranging: considers each 'slack' and 'surplus' in turn, differentiating between binding and loose constraints. Prints maximum change in RHS, and the shadow price of binding constraints.

PROCobj_ranging: considers each main variable x in turn, differentiating between basic and non-basic cases. Prints maximum changes in objective function coefficients.

Now type in the following alterations to the main program, and these two Procedures.

Program 6.5 SENSITY: LP as 2PHASE with ranging of RHS and Z coefficients

```
  5 REM SENSIT

 35 REM RANGING OF RHS AND OBJECTIVE FUNCTION COEFFICIENTS

130 PROCrhs_ranging
140 PROCobj_ranging
150 END
160
```

```
7000 DEF PROCrhs_ranging
7010 PRINT :PRINT "RHS RANGE WHICH PRESERVES BASIS"
7020 PRINT : PRINT TAB(11) "SHADOW    MAX RHS    MAX RHS"
7030 PRINT "INEQUALITY   PRICE   DECREASE  INCREASE"
7040 PRINT : J=N-L-G
7050 REPEAT
7060 REPEAT
7070 J=J+1
7080 IF J>N THEN ENDPROC
7090 IF STATUS(J)=1 THEN I=0 :REPEAT :I=I+1 :UNTIL A(I,0)=J
7100 II=J-N+L+G
7110 IF STATUS(J)=1 THEN PRINT STR$(II);" LOOSE";TAB(16);"-";
7120 IF STATUS(J)=1 AND TYPE$(II)="L" THEN PRINT TAB(20);C(I);
7130 IF STATUS(J)=1 AND TYPE$(II)="L" THEN PRINT TAB(30);"INF"
7140 IF STATUS(J)=1 AND TYPE$(II)="G" THEN PRINT TAB(20);"INF";
7150 IF STATUS(J)=1 AND TYPE$(II)="G" THEN PRINT TAB(30);C(I)
7160 UNTIL STATUS(J)=0
7170 INC = 10E8 : DEC = 10E8 : T=1E-08
7180 FOR I=1 TO L+G+E
7190 IF ABS(A(I,J))>T THEN LIMIT=C(I)/A(I,J) ELSE LIMIT=10E8
7200 IF A(I,J)<-T AND (-LIMIT)<INC THEN INC=-LIMIT
7210 IF A(I,J) > T AND LIMIT < DEC THEN DEC=LIMIT
7220 NEXT I
7230 PRINT STR$(II);" BINDING";TAB(12);A(0,J);
7240 IF TYPE$(II)="L" AND DEC<10E8 THEN PRINT TAB(20);DEC;
7250 IF TYPE$(II)="L" AND DEC=10E8 THEN PRINT TAB(20);"INF";
7260 IF TYPE$(II)="L" AND INC<10E8 THEN PRINT TAB(30);INC
7270 IF TYPE$(II)="L" AND INC=10E8 THEN PRINT TAB(30);"INF"
7280 IF TYPE$(II)="G" AND INC<10E8 THEN PRINT TAB(20);INC;
7290 IF TYPE$(II)="G" AND INC=10E8 THEN PRINT TAB(20);"INF";
7300 IF TYPE$(II)="G" AND DEC<10E8 THEN PRINT TAB(30);DEC
7310 IF TYPE$(II)="G" AND DEC=10E8 THEN PRINT TAB(30);"INF"
7320 UNTIL FALSE
7330 ENDPROC
7340
7500 DEF PROCobj_ranging
7510 PRINT :PRINT "OB FN COEFF RANGE WHICH PRESERVES BASIS"
7520 PRINT :PRINT "MAIN     ORIGINAL   MAX       MAX"
7530 PRINT "VARIABLE    COEFF   DECREASE  INCREASE"
7540 JJ=0
7550 REPEAT
7560 REPEAT
7570 JJ=JJ+1
7580 IF JJ > N-L-G THEN ENDPROC
7590 IF STATUS(JJ)=0 THEN PRINT "X";STR$(JJ);TAB(9);B(JJ);
7600 IF STATUS(JJ)=0 AND Z$="MAX" THEN PRINT TAB(20);"INF";
7610 IF STATUS(JJ)=0 AND Z$="MAX" THEN PRINT TAB(30);A(0,JJ)
7620 IF STATUS(JJ)=0 AND Z$="MIN" THEN PRINT TAB(20);A(0,JJ);
7630 IF STATUS(JJ)=0 AND Z$="MIN" THEN PRINT TAB(30);"INF"
7640 UNTIL STATUS(JJ)=1
7650 I =0
7660 REPEAT
7670 I=I+1
7680 UNTIL A(I,0) = JJ
7690 INC=10E8 : DEC=10E8 : T=1E-08
7700 FOR J=1 TO N
7710 IF STATUS(J)=0 AND ABS(A(I,J))>T THEN LIMIT=A(0,J)/A(I,J)
     ELSE LIMIT=10E8
7720 IF A(I,J) <-T AND (-LIMIT)<INC THEN INC=-LIMIT
7730 IF A(I,J) > T AND  LIMIT <DEC THEN DEC= LIMIT
7740 NEXT J
7750 PRINT "X";STR$(A(I,0));TAB(9);B(A(I,0));
7760 IF Z$="MAX" AND DEC<10E8 THEN PRINT TAB(20);DEC;
7770 IF Z$="MAX" AND DEC=10E8 THEN PRINT TAB(20);"INF";
7780 IF Z$="MAX" AND INC<10E8 THEN PRINT TAB(30);INC
7790 IF Z$="MAX" AND INC=10E8 THEN PRINT TAB(30);"INF"
7800 IF Z$="MIN" AND INC<10E8 THEN PRINT TAB(20);INC;
7810 IF Z$="MIN" AND INC=10E8 THEN PRINT TAB(20);"INF";
7820 IF Z$="MIN" AND DEC<10E8 THEN PRINT TAB(30);DEC
7830 IF Z$="MIN" AND DEC=10E8 THEN PRINT TAB(30);"INF"
7840 UNTIL JJ=N-L-G
7850 ENDPROC
```

When satisfied with the accuracy of your listing you should RUN with the data of problem P2. The final part of the printout is given below.

RHS RANGE WHICH PRESERVES BASIS

INEQUALITY	SHADOW PRICE	MAX RHS DECREASE	MAX RHS INCREASE
1 BINDING	1.667	150.000	300.000
2 LOOSE	-	100.000	INF
3 BINDING	0.333	150.000	150.000
4 LOOSE	-	INF	100.000

OB FN COEFF RANGE WHICH PRESERVES BASIS

MAIN VARIABLE	ORIGINAL COEFF	MAX DECREASE	MAX INCREASE
X1	3.000	1.000	INF
X2	1.000	INF	0.500

The post-optimal analysis contains some very important management information. The RHS ranging analysis was applied to the four constraints, Working capital (constraint 1), Bought-in items (constraint 2), Normal time working (constraint 3), and the Process constraint (constraint 4). The printout tells us firstly that for every additional monetary unit of working capital up to a maximum of 300 additional mu, an extra contribution of 1.667 mu is possible. Conversely, a reduction of up to 150mu will reduce the contribution in the same proportion. Secondly, there are sufficient bought-in items for the production of a further 100 units of product 2. Thirdly, for each hour reduction (increase) in normal time working there is an increase (decrease) in the contribution of 0.333 mu for changes of up to 150 hours over the planning period. Finally, the minimum process rate of product 1 production is comfortably exceeded.

The ranging of the objective function coefficients shows that the current basis stays optimal if the profit contribution of product 1 is in excess of 2 mu; it is also optimal if the profit contribution of the second product is less than 1.5 mu.

You should do the remaining Problems now.

Problems

(6.1) Modify Program ENUMER to pick out the optimum basis and objective function value for Maximize and Minimize problems. Test your program on the data for problems P1 and P2.

(6.2) Devise a PROCread which reads data from DATA statements, as an alternative which can be exercised at the user's discretion to conversational data input in PROCinput.

(6.3) Devise a PROCedit to be called from the main program of SIMPLEX which enables the user to change any of the input data, until the user is satisfied, whereupon set Q$='N'.

```
84 REPEAT
85 PROCedit
86 UNTIL Q$ = "N"
```
N.B. PROCedit must call PROCprint.

(6.4) Devise a PROCsoln for SIMPLEX which prints out the value of z and the values of the basic variables in the optimum solution.

(6.5) Devise an improvement which allows the user to give names to main variables and to constraint rows. Incorporate the naming of variables into PROCsoln of Problem 6.4, and extend PROCsoln to provide the values of the slack variables for named rows.

(6.6) RUN SIMPLEX to observe *cycling* with E.M.L. Beale's example:

$$\text{MIN } z = -.75x_1 + 20x_2 - .5x_3 + 6x_4$$
$$\text{Subject to} \quad .25x_1 - 8x_2 - x_3 + 9x_4 <= 0$$
$$.5x_1 - 12x_2 - .5x_3 + 3x_4 <= 0$$
$$x_3 <= 1$$

(6.7) Devise a PROCalternative which is called in line 129 of SIMPLEX when there exist one or more non-basic variables j at the optimum solution such that $A(0,j)$ is near zero. The user should be given the option of entering j into the basis.

(6.8) Use 2PHASE to solve the following L.P. problem, which is an example of the so-called 'diet' problem described by E.M.L. Beale in *Mathematical Programming in Practice*, Pitman, 1968.

$$\text{Minimize } z = 4x_1 + 5x_2 + 7x_3 + 6x_4$$
$$\text{Subject to} \quad x_1 + x_2 + x_3 + x_4 = 1$$
$$5x_2 + 3x_3 + 5x_4 >= 2$$
$$x_2 + 2x_3 + 2x_4 >= 1$$
$$10x_1 + 4x_3 + 2x_4 = 5$$
$$4x_2 + x_3 + x_4 <= 2$$

(6.9) RUN SENSITY with numerical examples drawn from standard textbooks. You can redimension the program to cater for larger problems. Using M+1 rows and N+M+1 columns a standard BBC B micro can cope with a problem with, say, 20 rows and 20 main variables in, say, 5 minutes, but you should beware problems due to rounding errors and ill-conditioning.

(6.10) RUN SENSITY for problem P2 with the additional equality constraint $x_1 - x_2 = 0$. Superimpose this equality constraint upon Figure 6.4 to check your output.

(6.11) Write a PROCknown_basis which generates a first simplex tableau from a set of user input basic variable indices. (Hint: draw upon ENUMER for the Gaussian elimination procedures.)

(6.12) Re-draw the eight feasible regions for each of the eight changes in the constraints indicated by the RHS ranging analysis in the text. Then re-draw the original feasible region and superimpose the four instances of objective function lines, which apply at the extremes of the ranging of the objective function coefficients.

(6.13) Write a management report upon your interpretation of the results of the post-optimal analysis of the RUN to problem P2 which was given in the text.

(6.14) Readers who understand the definition of a linear programming problem of 'transportation type' should write the following procedures: PROCtlp_input and PROCtlp_matrix. The former should allow the user to input the number of origins and destinations, the availabilities and requirements, and the transportation cost coefficients. The latter generates the matrix of constraint coefficients automatically.

Chapter 7

Markov chains

Essential theory

7.1 Introduction to Markov chains

A Markov chain model may be usefully employed for the analysis of a system with both dynamic and probabilistic features. Suppose that a system can be in one of a finite number of states, and its behaviour can be modelled as a probabilistic trajectory through intermediate states at some suitably chosen instances, which may be regular or irregular points in time. A discrete valued state variable s_i is associated with the ith system state for $i=0,1,2,\ldots,I$. This state variable s_i is distinguished from a discrete valued stage variable n. Variable n is used to convey the idea that the state of the system is examined at successive discrete instances $n=0,1,2,\ldots,N$ where the initial examination occurs at stage $n = 0$.

A Markov chain has the property that the random change from state s_i at stage n to s_j at stage $n+1$ does not depend in any way upon the state trajectory which developed prior to stage n. So this random change of state accords with the conditional probability distribution

Probability (state s_j at stage $n+1$/state s_i at stage n) = $P_{i,j}$
for all stages $n = 0,1,2,\ldots,N-1$

Thus Markov chains are said to have a 'stationary set of transition probabilities'; i.e. independent of the stage variable. Transitions between each pair of states may occur in principle and so a square conditional probability transition matrix P can be defined with non-negative conditional transition probabilities. The matrix P has order $I+1$, where the rows correspond to the state at stage n and the columns to the state at stage $n+1$. Conditional transition probabilities for certain or impossible transitions are 1 and 0 respectively and since a transition must occur between successive stages, if only to the same state, the entries in the rows of the matrix P sum to unity.

113

7.2 An illustrative example

Suppose, for illustration, that a machine has a random tendency to deteriorate instantaneously from a state s_0 'properly adjusted' at the start of a period of operation to s_1 'poorly adjusted' just prior to the end of the period. If the periods are the duration of a working shift, say, then the stages correspond to the intervals between shifts. The machine is assumed to be 'properly adjusted' before the start of the first shift, i.e. at stage 0. A machine which is 'properly adjusted' at the start of a shift produces 100 items of acceptable quality in that shift. A machine which is 'poorly adjusted' at the start of a shift produces 90 acceptable items in that shift. Management needs to know what level of acceptable output to expect from a shift. A machine which is in state s_1 'poorly adjusted' at the start of a shift may deteriorate instantaneously to the state s_2 'inoperable' just prior to the end of the shift. An 'inoperable' machine always receives attention for the duration of the next shift and it is returned to the state s_0 'properly adjusted' by the end. The matrix of stationary transition probabilities is given in Table 7.1.

Table 7.1   A matrix of transition probabilities

		s_0	s_1	s_3
	s_0	0.9	0.1	
$P =$	s_1		0.75	0.25
	s_2	1		

Notice that there is a probability $P_{0,1} = 0.1$ that a 'properly adjusted' machine at the start of a shift is 'poorly adjusted' at the start of the next shift. There is an even larger probability $P_{1,2} = 0.25$ that a machine which is 'poorly adjusted' at the start of a shift is 'inoperable' at the start of the next. The element $P_{2,0} = 1$ in the third row follows from the definitions of state and stage, i.e. it is certain that a machine which is 'inoperative' at the start of a shift is 'properly adjusted' at the start of the next.

A comprehensive set of system trajectories over the first three shifts is provided in Figure 7.1. There are 2, 4 and 7 trajectories from state s_0 to the system states at stages 1, 2 and 3. The reader can extend the figure to check that there are 12 trajectories to the system states at stage 4. All the non-zero transition probabilities are shown, and the trajectories have probabilities which are calculated from the product of the appropriate transition probabilities.

The n-stage probability $^nP_{i,j}$ of achieving state s_j at stage n by a trajectory from state s_i at stage 0 is given by the sum of the

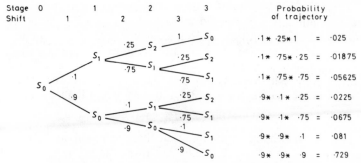

Figure 7.1 The system state trajectories over three transitions

appropriate trajectory probabilities. For example, it is evident from Figure 7.1 that the machine is in state s_1 'poorly adjusted' at stage 3 with probability.

$$^3P_{o,1} = .05625 + .0675 + .081 = .20475$$

But it is much easier to calculate $^nP_{i,j}$ recursively. The probability associated with an n-stage trajectory to state s_j from state s_i at stage 0 can be obtained from the sum of products, over all k, of the probabilities of the $n-1$ stage trajectory to state s_k and the single-stage transition from s_k to s_j. Thus

$$^nP_{i,j} = \sum_k {}^{n-1}P_{i,k} * P_{k,j} \text{ for } n = 2,3, \ldots, N$$

where $^1P_{i,j} = P_{i,j}$

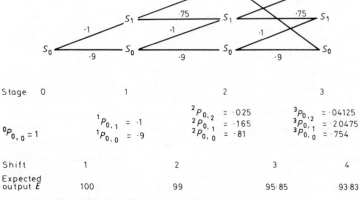

Figure 7.2 State diagram over three transitions, $^nP_{0,j}$ and E

This idea is synonymous with redrawing Figure 7.1 so that each state is uniquely represented at each stage, with the result that individual trajectories are no longer discernible. This is done in Figure 7.2, which also gives the probabilities $^nP_{i,j}$ for $n = 1,2,3$ from recursive calculations. Now the expected output in the nth shift, E, can be written as follows, and this expression was used for the calculations of E for $n = 2,3,4$ also shown in Figure 7.2:

$$E_n = 100 * {}^{n-1}P_{0,0} + 90 * {}^{n-1}P_{0.1} + 0 * {}^{n-1}P_{0,2}$$

It is not necessary to assume that the machine is in state 0 at stage 0. Its initial state could be taken as a vector $^0p'$ of probabilities, and in general we can think of the state of the machine at stage n as the vector $^np'$ where

$$^np' = (\text{Prob. of } s_0, \text{ Prob. of } s_1, \ldots, \text{Prob. of } s_I)$$

A recursion can then be written compactly using matrix algebra

$$^np' = {}^{n-1}p'P$$

for $n = 1,2, \ldots, N$.

If an output vector is denoted by e where $e = (100, 90, 0)$ then the output E_n in the nth shift is given by

$$E_n = {}^{n-1}p'\, e$$

In the present example, one finds that

$$
\begin{aligned}
^0p' &= (\quad 1, \quad\quad 0, \quad\quad 0) \text{ and } E_1 = 100 \\
^1p' &= (\quad .9, \quad\quad .1, \quad\quad 0) \quad\quad E_2 = 99 \\
^2p' &= (\quad .81, \quad .165, \quad .025) \quad E_3 = 95.85 \\
^3p' &= (\ .754, .20475, .04125) \quad E_4 = 93.83
\end{aligned}
$$

The elements of the vectors $^np'$ and the values of E accord with the n-stage probabilities and expected outputs from Figure 7.2 above. Now a solution to the recursion is obviously

$$^np' = {}^0p'\, P^n$$

for $n = 1,2, \ldots, N$.

The first row of P^n corresponds to $^np'$ when the initial state vector $^0p' = (1,0,0)$, the second row of P^n to $^0p' = (0,1,0)$, and the third row to $^0p' = (0,0,1)$. Thus the rows of P^n contain in vector form the n-stage probabilities $^nP_{i,j}$ for all $j = 0,1,2, \ldots, I$. If the rows of P^n are similar then the vector $^np'$ is not closely dependent upon the initial state. If the difference between the individual rows of P^n, and the difference between each row of P^n and the corresponding row of P^{n+1} both reduce as n increases then there is *a priori* evidence of a 'steady state', i.e. that the state vector of probabilities settles into a form for large n which is independent of the stage and the initial state. This is discussed more fully later on.

The program MARKOV consists of the following PROCE-DURES:

PROCinput: allows the user to enter the total number of system states I+1, the maximum number of stages N, the elements of the array $v(0,i)$ which is used to store the initial state vector $^0p'$ and the elements of the array $P(i,j)$ which is used to store the matrix of transition probabilities P.

PROCstate_vector: uses the equation $^np'=^{n-1}p'P$ to find the vectors $^np'$ recursively for $n = 1,2, \ldots ,N$ and stores them as rows of a two-dimensional array $v(n,i)$.

PROCnstage_matrix: finds and prints the nth power P^n of P for $n = 1,2, \ldots ,N$ which is stored as a three-dimensional array n_stage(i,j,n).

Type in MARKOV from the listing below.

118

Program 7.2A MARKOV: Markov chain analysis for first N stages

```
  10 REM MARKOV
  20 REM FINDS FIRST N VECTORS OF STATE PROBABILITIES
  30 REM FINDS FIRST N POWERS OF TRANSITION MATRIX P^n
  40 DIM v(10,9),P(9,9),n_stage(9,9,10)
  50 @%=&0002060A
  60
  70 PROCinput
  80 PROCstate_vector
  90 PROCnstage_matrix
 100 END
 110
1000 DEF PROCinput
1010 INPUT "ENTER THE TOTAL NUMBER OF SYSTEM STATES ",I
1020 I = I-1
1030 INPUT "ENTER THE MAXIMUM NUMBER OF STAGES ",N
1040 PRINT "ENTER THE ELEMENTS OF THE INITIAL STATE VECTOR"
1050 FOR i = 0 TO I
1060 PRINT "p(";STR$(i);") = " ; : INPUT v(0,i)
1070 NEXT i
1080 PRINT
1090 PRINT "ENTER THE ELEMENTS OF THE TRANSITION MATRIX"
1100 FOR i = 0 TO I
1110 FOR j = 0 TO I
1120 PRINT "P(";STR$(i);",";STR$(j);") = " ; : INPUT P(i,j)
1130 n_stage(i,j,1) = P(i,j)
1140 NEXT j
1150 NEXT i
1160 ENDPROC
1170
1500 DEF PROCstate_vector
1510 PRINT : PRINT "STAGE        STATE  PROBABILITY VECTOR"
1520 FOR n = 1 TO N
1530 FOR j = 0 TO I
1540 FOR i = 0 TO I
1550 v(n,j) = v(n,j) + v(n-1,i) * P(i,j)
1560 NEXT i
1570 NEXT j
1580 PRINT STR$(n) TAB(7) "(";
1590 FOR j = 0 TO I
1600 PRINT v(n,j) ;
1610 NEXT j
1620 PRINT ")"
1630 NEXT n
1640 ENDPROC
1650
2000 DEF PROCnstage_matrix
2010 FOR n = 2 TO N
2020 PRINT:PRINT STR$(n)"-STAGE TRANSITION MATRIX P``";STR$(n)
2030 FOR i = 0 TO I
2040 FOR j = 0 TO I
2050 FOR k = 0 TO I
2060 n_stage(i,j,n) = n_stage(i,j,n) + P(i,k) * n_stage(k,j,n-1)
2070 NEXT k
2080 PRINT n_stage(i,j,n) ;
2090 NEXT j
2100 PRINT ""
2110 NEXT i
2120 NEXT n
2130 ENDPROC
2140

  RUN
ENTER THE TOTAL NUMBER OF SYSTEM STATES ?3
ENTER THE MAXIMUM NUMBER OF STAGES ?7
ENTER THE ELEMENTS OF THE INITIAL STATE VECTOR
p(0) = ?1
p(1) = ?0
p(2) = ?0
```

```
ENTER THE ELEMENTS OF THE TRANSITION MATRIX
P(0,0) = ?.9
P(0,1) = ?.1
P(0,2) = ?0
P(1,0) = ?0
P(1,1) = ?.75
P(1,2) = ?.25
P(2,0) = ?1
P(2,1) = ?0
P(2,2) = ?0

STAGE          STATE PROBABILITY VECTOR
1       (  0.900000   0.100000   0.000000)
2       (  0.810000   0.165000   0.025000)
3       (  0.754000   0.204750   0.041250)
4       (  0.719850   0.228962   0.051187)
5       (  0.699052   0.243707   0.057241)
6       (  0.686388   0.252685   0.060927)
7       (  0.678676   0.258153   0.063171)

2-STAGE TRANSITION MATRIX P^2
   0.810000   0.165000   0.025000
   0.250000   0.562500   0.187500
   0.900000   0.100000   0.000000

3-STAGE TRANSITION MATRIX P^3
   0.754000   0.204750   0.041250
   0.412500   0.446875   0.140625
   0.810000   0.165000   0.025000

4-STAGE TRANSITION MATRIX P^4
   0.719850   0.228962   0.051187
   0.511875   0.376406   0.111719
   0.754000   0.204750   0.041250

5-STAGE TRANSITION MATRIX P^5
   0.699052   0.243707   0.057241
   0.572406   0.333492   0.094102
   0.719850   0.228962   0.051187

6-STAGE TRANSITION MATRIX P^6
   0.686388   0.252685   0.060927
   0.609267   0.307360   0.083373
   0.699052   0.243707   0.057241

7-STAGE TRANSITION MATRIX P^7
   0.678676   0.258153   0.063171
   0.631714   0.291447   0.076840
   0.686388   0.252685   0.060927
```

You should duplicate the RUN when you are satisfied with the accuracy of your listing. If you should try other RUNs with more than 10 stages or 10 states you should first redimension the arrays in line 40. Do Problems 7.1 and 7.2 here.

There is strong *a priori* evidence of the gradual approach of steady state conditions. The idea of a steady state is synonymous with redrawing Figure 7.2 as in Figure 7.3. The transition probabilities are written alongside the arrows, which convey the sense of progression from one stage to the next.

If steady state conditions do occur then the superscript can be dropped from the state vector to yield an equation in the steady state vector of probabilities p':

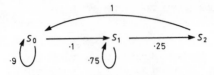

Figure 7.3 State transitions under steady state conditions

$$p' = p'P$$
or $p'\,(P-I) = 0'$ where $0'$ is a null vector

These equations are written out in full for the numerical example of this section, using the notation $p' = (p_0, p_1, p_2)$

$$
\begin{aligned}
-.1\,p_0 + \ \ 0\ \ p_1 + 1\,p_2 &= 0 \\
.1\,p_0 - .25\,p_1 + 0\,p_2 &= 0 \\
0\,p_0 + .25\,p_1 - 1\,p_2 &= 0
\end{aligned}
$$

These steady state equations can be given a 'flow' interpretation. Figure 7.4 is similar to Figure 7.3 but the elements of the matrix $P-I$ are written alongside the arrows. In the steady state there is a zero rate of change in stage dependent probability. So in the case of state s_0, say the 'flow rate into state s_0' of $1\,p_2$ must equal the 'flow rate out of state s_0' of $.1\,p_0$. The equality between these flow rates yields the first steady state equation. A similar analogy for s_1 and s_2 yields the second and third steady state equations respectively.

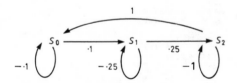

Figure 7.4 Flow analogy for steady state equations

Notice that these three equations are not linearly independent (e.g. the third is the negative sum of the first two). This will be the case in general, and the following 'normalizing condition' can be substituted for any one of them

$$p_0 + p_1 + p_2 = 1$$

These steady state equations are very easy to solve here. The second and third yield

$$p_1 = 2/5\,p_0 \text{ and } p_2 = 1/10\,p_0$$

The application of the 'normalizing condition' gives

$$p_0 = 2/3, \ p_1 = 4/15, \ p_2 = 1/15$$

The long run output of parts of acceptable quality is 90.67 per shift, from substituting the steady state probabilities into the former expression for E.

In general, the steady state equations may be solved by Gaussian elimination. The approach here is to borrow the appropriate PROCEDURES from Program ENUMER of the preceding chapter.

PROCsteady_state: sets up the matrix of coefficients A and the right-hand side vector C for the steady state equations $Ap' = C$, having substituted the normalizing equation for the final steady state equation. Calls other procedures from line 3000 *et seq*.

Make the following amendments to Program MARKOV.

```
10 REM LONGRUN

35 REM FINDS STEADY STATE PROBABILITIES
40 DIM v(10,9),P(9,9),n_stage(9,9,10),p(9),A(9,9),C(9)

85 PROCsteady_state
```

Now type in lines 2500 *et seq* from the listing below.

Program 7.2B LONGRUN: Finds steady state probability vector

```
  10 REM LONGRUN
  20 REM FINDS FIRST N VECTORS OF STATE PROBABILITIES
  30 REM FINDS FIRST N POWERS OF TRANSITION MATRIX P^n
  35 REM FINDS STEADY STATE PROBABILITIES
  40 DIM v(10,9),P(9,9),n_stage(9,9,10),p(9),A(9,9),C(9)
  50 @%=&0002060A
  60
  70 PROCinput
  80 PROCstate_vector
  85 PROCsteady_state
  90 PROCnstage_matrix
 100 END
 110
1000 DEF PROCinput
1010 INPUT "ENTER THE TOTAL NUMBER OF SYSTEM STATES ",I
1020 I = I-1
1030 INPUT "ENTER THE MAXIMUM NUMBER OF STAGES ",N
1040 PRINT "ENTER THE ELEMENTS OF THE INITIAL STATE VECTOR"
1050 FOR i = 0 TO I
1060 PRINT "p(";STR$(i);") = " ; : INPUT v(0,i)
1070 NEXT i
1080 PRINT
1090 PRINT "ENTER THE ELEMENTS OF THE TRANSITION MATRIX"
1100 FOR i = 0 TO I
1110 FOR j = 0 TO I
1120 PRINT "P(";STR$(i);",";STR$(j);") = " ; : INPUT P(i,j)
1130 n_stage(i,j,1) = P(i,j)
1140 NEXT j
1150 NEXT i
1160 ENDPROC
1170
1500 DEF PROCstate_vector
1510 PRINT : PRINT "STAGE       STATE PROBABILITY VECTOR"
1520 FOR n = 1 TO N
1530 FOR j = 0 TO I
1540 FOR i = 0 TO I
1550 v(n,j) = v(n,j) + v(n-1,i) * P(i,j)
1560 NEXT i
1570 NEXT j
1580 PRINT STR$(n) TAB(7) "(";
1590 FOR j = 0 TO I
1600 PRINT v(n,j) ;
1610 NEXT j
1620 PRINT ")"
1630 NEXT n
1640 ENDPROC
1650
2000 DEF PROCnstage_matrix
2010 FOR n = 2 TO N
2020 PRINT:PRINT STR$(n)"-STAGE TRANSITION MATRIX P^";STR$(n)
2030 FOR i = 0 TO I
2040 FOR j = 0 TO I
2050 FOR k = 0 TO I
2060 n_stage(i,j,n) = n_stage(i,j,n) + P(i,k) * n_stage(k,j,n-1)
2070 NEXT k
2080 PRINT n_stage(i,j,n) ;
2090 NEXT j
2100 PRINT ""
2110 NEXT i
2120 NEXT n
2130 ENDPROC
2140
```

```
2500 DEF PROCsteady_state
2510 FOR i = 0 TO I-1
2520 FOR j = 0 TO I
2530 A(i,j) = P(j,i)
2540 NEXT j
2550 A(i,i) = A(i,i) - 1
2560 C(i) = 0
2570 NEXT i
2580 FOR j = 0 TO I
2590 A(I,j) = 1
2600 NEXT j
2610 C(I) = 1
2620 PROCgauss
2630 ENDPROC
2640
3000 DEF PROCgauss
3010 FOR k= 0 TO I-1
3020 PROCfind_pivot
3030 IF r>k THEN PROCinterchange_rows
3040 PROCelimination
3050 NEXT k
3060 PROCback_subst
3070 ENDPROC
3080
3500 DEF PROCfind_pivot
3510 d=0 : r=k
3520 FOR i = k TO I
3530 c = ABS(A(i,k))
3540 IF d < c THEN d=c : r=i
3550 NEXT i
3560 ENDPROC
3570
4000 DEF PROCinterchange_rows
4010 FOR j = k TO I
4020 d = A(k,j)
4030 A(k,j) = A(r,j)
4040 A(r,j) = d
4050 NEXT j
4060 d = C(k)
4070 C(k) = C(r)
4080 C(r) = d
4090 ENDPROC
4100
4500 DEF PROCelimination
4510 FOR i = k+1 TO I
4520 d = -A(i,k)/A(k,k)
4530 FOR j = 1 TO I
4540 A(i,j) = A(i,j) + d*A(k,j)
4550 NEXT j
4560 C(i) = C(i) + d*C(k)
4570 NEXT i
4580 ENDPROC
4590
5000 DEF PROCback_subst
5010 IF A(I,I)=0 THEN PRINT "SINGULAR P-I" : ENDPROC
5020 p(I)=C(I)/A(I,I)
5030 FOR i = I-1 TO 0 STEP -1
5040 d=C(i)
5050 FOR j= i+1 TO I
5060 d=d-A(i,j)*p(j)
5070 NEXT j
5080 p(i) = d/A(i,i)
5090 NEXT i
5100 PRINT : PRINT TAB(12) "STEADY STATE VECTOR"
5110 PRINT TAB(7) "(";
5120 FOR i = 0 TO I
5130 PRINT p(i);
5140 NEXT i
5150 PRINT ")"
5160 ENDPROC
```

A RUN with the data for the numerical example of this section should corroborate the earlier calculations of the steady state probability vector. Now do Problems 7.3 to 7.7.

7.3 Maintenance policies

It is often cheaper to schedule preventative maintenance, rather than incur the costs of unexpected breakdown. Suppose that the data of Table 7.2 has been obtained for the 'number of periods completed prior to failure' from a trial of 100 identical machines

Table 7.2   Failure data

Number of completed periods before failure	Number of machines	Failure probability	Conditional failure probability $^*p_i$
0	20	.2	20/100 = .2
1	20	.2	20/80 = .25
2	24	.24	24/60 = .4
3	18	.18	18/36 = .5
4	9	.09	9/18 = .5
5	9	.09	9/9 = 1.0

If it is assumed that failures occur just prior to the end of a period then the average service life is given by the quantity

$$1\times.2 + 2\times.2 + 3\times.24 + 4\times.18 + 5\times.09 + 6\times.09 = 3.03$$
periods

If it is further assumed that a repair can be completed prior to the start of the next period and that the subsequent failure probability distribution reverts to that of a new machine, then in the absence of preventative maintenance one would find a long-run failure probability $= 3.03^{-1} = .33$ per period. This gives rise to an expected cost of $.33 \times 350 = £115.51$ per period for the cost data of Table 7.3.

Table 7.3   Cost data

Cost of repair per failure	£350
Cost of scheduled maintenance	£ 25

One might expect that preventative maintenance policies could be devised to reduce this expected long-run cost. Such policies fall into two classes:

C1 Maintain n periods after the machine last received attention
C2 Maintain the machine after n calendar periods

For an example of the first class of policy one could cite the maintenance schedules for an aircraft engine, say, which is overhauled after a prescribed number of flying hours have been completed either since the previous overhaul or since a repair was effected. The second class of policy is much easier to administer because it is not necessary to keep detailed service histories for individual machines. One may choose for example to service equipment on an annual basis.

These two classes of policy are considered separately in the following sections.

7.4 Maintain *n* periods after the machine last received attention

The steady state behaviour of Markov chains can be employed to model the long-run performance of this first class of preventative maintenance policy. The stages correspond to the time between periods. The states are defined as the number of periods of consecutive use without attention. Table 7.4 shows the non-zero elements of the conditional probability matrix using the data from the final column of Table 7.2. It is explicitly assumed that any failures occur at the end of a period of operation and that repairs are effected in time for the start of the next period. Furthermore, the repair or maintenance of a machine provides a future failure distribution which is the same as that of a new machine.

Table 7.4   Transition matrix P: no scheduled maintenance

		Periods completed without attention at stage $k+1$					
		0	1	2	3	4	5
Periods	0	.2	.8				
completed	1	.25		.75			
without	2	.4			.6		
attention	3	.5				.5	
at stage	4	.5					.5
k	5	1.0					

The steady state vector $p' = (p_0, p_1, p_2, p_3, p_4, p_5)$ can be found from program LONGRUN. The first element is $p_0 = .33$ which is interpreted as the long-run probability that a machine commences a period of operation having just been repaired. Note that no preventative maintenance is possible if machines are allowed to commence a sixth period of operation as in the matrix of Table 7.4. The value of p_0 gives confirmation of the long-run probability of failure per period given in the last section.

If, however, preventative maintenance is scheduled after 5 periods of machine operation without failure then the associated transition matrix P is given in Table 7.5.

Table 7.5   Transition matrix P: Maintenance scheduled after $n = 5$ consecutive periods of operation

		Periods completed without attention at stage $k+1$				
		0	1	2	3	4
Periods	0	.2	.8			
completed	1	.25		.75		
without	2	.4			.6	
attention	3	.5				.5
at stage k	4	1.0				

Another RUN of LONGRUN with the data of Table 7.5 yields a value of $p_0 = .34$. But this cannot be interpreted simply as the failure probability here. State s_0 is achieved whenever the machine has just received attention, either because it has failed or because it has been maintained. Instead, an expression for the failure probability f can be written as follows, using the vector notation $*p$ for the conditional probabilities $*p_i$ of the final column of Table 7.2:

$$f = p' \, *p$$
$$= (.340\,136, .272\,109, .204\,082, .122\,449, .061\,224)' \quad * $$
$$(.2, .25, .4, .5, .5)$$
$$= .309\,524$$

This expression sums the products of the steady state probabilities with the conditional probabilities of failure in these states during the forthcoming period. Notice that f is smaller than was the case without preventative maintenance.

Now the probability of maintenance m is given by

$$m = p_4 \times (1 - *p_4) = .061\,224 \times .5 = .030\,612$$

The expected cost per period C_5 of scheduled maintenance after 5 periods in use is given by

$$C_5 = 350\,f + 25\,m = £\,109.10$$

Thus it is marginally cheaper to maintain after 5 periods in use than not to maintain the machine at all. But the best policy will have the lowest value of C_n for $n = 1,2,3,4,5,6$. Program SCHEDC1 below carries out these calculations. Make the following alterations to LONGRUN.

```
  10 REM SCHEDC1
  20 REM MACHINE FAILURES AT PERIOD END ARE REPAIRED
  30 REM FINDS COST OF SCHEDULED MAINTENANCE   CLASS C1
  35 REM EVERY n PERIODS OF UNINTERUPTED USE
  40 DIM P(9,9),p(9),A(9,9),C(9)

  75 n = I
  80 FOR I = 1 TO n
  85 PROCsteady_state
  90 NEXT I

1030 INPUT "ENTER THE COST OF REPAIR PER FAILURE ",F
1040 INPUT "ENTER THE COST OF MAINTENANCE ",M

DELETE 1050 to 1070  DELETE 1130  DELETE 1500 to 2140

2575 A(0,I) = 1
5100 cost = F*P(0,0) + M*( 1-P(0,0) )
5110 IF I=1 THEN PRINT "Maintain after 1 period  costs ";cost
5120 f = 0
5130 FOR i = 0 TO I
5140 f = f + p(i) * P(i,0)
5150 NEXT i
5160 m = p(I) * (1-P(I,0))
5170 cost = F * f  + M * m
5180 PRINT "Maintain after ";STR$(I+1);" periods costs ";cost
5190 ENDPROC
```

Now check your program against the listing of SCHEDC1 below, and a RUN with the data of Tables 7.3 and 7.4 should confirm the results in Table 7.6, which follows the listing.

Program 7.4 SCHEDC1: preventative maintenance class C1

```
  10 REM SCHEDC1
  20 REM MACHINE FAILURES AT PERIOD END ARE REPAIRED
  30 REM FINDS COST OF SCHEDULED MAINTENANCE   CLASS C1
  35 REM EVERY n PERIODS OF UNINTERUPTED USE
  40 DIM P(9,9),p(9),A(9,9),C(9)
  50 @%=&0002060A
  60
  70 PROCinput
  75 n = I
  80 FOR I = 1 TO n
  85 PROCsteady_state
  90 NEXT I
 100 END
 110
1000 DEF PROCinput
1010 INPUT "ENTER THE TOTAL NUMBER OF SYSTEM STATES ",I
1020 I = I-1
1030 INPUT "ENTER THE COST OF REPAIR PER FAILURE ",F
1040 INPUT "ENTER THE COST OF MAINTENANCE ",M
1080 PRINT
1090 PRINT "ENTER THE ELEMENTS OF THE TRANSITION MATRIX"
1100 FOR i = 0 TO I
1110 FOR j = 0 TO I
1120 PRINT "P(";STR$(i);",";STR$(j);") = " ; : INPUT P(i,j)
1140 NEXT j
1150 NEXT i
1160 ENDPROC
1170
```

```
2500 DEF PROCsteady_state
2510 FOR i = 0 TO I-1
2520 FOR j = 0 TO I
2530 A(i,j) = P(j,i)
2540 NEXT j
2550 A(i,i) = A(i,i) - 1
2560 C(i) = 0
2570 NEXT i
2575 A(0,I) = 1
2580 FOR j = 0 TO I
2590 A(I,j) = 1
2600 NEXT j
2610 C(I) = 1
2620 PROCgauss
2630 ENDPROC
2640
3000 DEF PROCgauss
3010 FOR k= 0 TO I-1
3020 PROCfind_pivot
3030 IF r>k THEN PROCinterchange_rows
3040 PROCelimination
3050 NEXT k
3060 PROCback_subst
3070 ENDPROC
3080
3500 DEF PROCfind_pivot
3510 d=0 : r=k
3520 FOR i = k TO I
3530 c = ABS(A(i,k))
3540 IF d < c THEN d=c : r=i
3550 NEXT i
3560 ENDPROC
3570
4000 DEF PROCinterchange_rows
4010 FOR j = k TO I
4020 d = A(k,j)
4030 A(k,j) = A(r,j)
4040 A(r,j) = d
4050 NEXT j
4060 d = C(k)
4070 C(k) = C(r)
4080 C(r) = d
4090 ENDPROC
4100
4500 DEF PROCelimination
4510 FOR i = k+1 TO I
4520 d = -A(i,k)/A(k,k)
4530 FOR j = 1 TO I
4540 A(i,j) = A(i,j) + d*A(k,j)
4550 NEXT j
4560 C(i) = C(i) + d*C(k)
4570 NEXT i
4580 ENDPROC
4590
5000 DEF PROCback_subst
5010 IF A(I,I)=0 THEN PRINT "SINGULAR P-I" : ENDPROC
5020 p(I)=C(I)/A(I,I)
5030 FOR i = I-1 TO 0 STEP -1
5040 d=C(i)
5050 FOR j = i+1 TO I
5060 d=d-A(i,j)*p(j)
5070 NEXT j
5080 p(i) = d/A(i,i)
5090 NEXT i
5100 cost = F*P(0,0) + M*( 1-P(0,0) )
5110 IF I=1 THEN PRINT "Maintain after 1 period  costs `";cost
5120 f = 0
5130 FOR i = 0 TO I
5140 f = f + p(i) * P(i,0)
5150 NEXT i
5160 m = p(I) * (1-P(I,0))
5170 cost = F * f  + M * m
5180 PRINT "Maintain after ";STR$(I+1);" periods costs £";cost
5190 ENDPROC
```

Table 7.6 Cost of preventative maintenance policies class C1 from a RUN of SCHEDC1 with data of Tables 7.3 and 7.4

Maintain after n consecutive periods in operation	Expected cost
1[1]	£ 90.00
2	£ 86.11
3	£ 97.08
4	£105.62
5	£109.10
6[2]	£115.51

Notes
[1]The machine always starts a period 'as new', thus $f = .2$ $m = .8$.
[2]The case of 'no maintenance'.

It is seen from this table that the best policy is to maintain after two consecutive periods of machine operation. Now do Problem 7.8.

7.5 Maintain the machine after n calendar periods

If a machine is maintained every n calendar periods whatever the service history may be then the expected number of machine failures f_n in the n periods can be obtained as a sum of n-stage transition probabilities as follows

$$f_n = {}^1P_{0,0} + {}^2P_{0,0} + \ldots + {}^nP_{0,0}$$

Thus the expected cost per period C_n is given by

$$C_n = (350\,f_n + 25)/n$$

If $n = 4$ then a RUN of MARKOV with the data of Table 7.4 (with states now defined as 'calendar periods since last maintenance') gives

$$f_4 = .2 + .24 + .328 + .3416 = 1.1096$$

and so

$$C_4 = (1.1096 \times 350 + 25)/4 = £103.34$$

The best value of n can be determined from a comparison of the C_n for $n = 1,2,...,6$. Program SCHEDC2 below carries out these calculations. Make the following alterations to MARKOV.

```
10 REM SCHEDC2
20 REM MACHINE FAILURES AT PERIOD END ARE REPAIRED
30 REM FINDS COST OF SCHEDULED MAINTENANCE CLASS C2
35 REM EVERY n CALENDAR PERIODS
40 DIM v(10,9),P(9,9)

90 PROCcost
```

```
1030 v(0,0) = 1
1040 INPUT "ENTER THE COST OF REPAIR PER FAILURE ",F
1050 INPUT "ENTER THE COST OF MAINTENANCE ",M
1060 PRINT "ENTER THE MAXIMUM LENGTH OF THE MAINTENANCE"
1070 INPUT "CYCLE IN PERIODS ",N
```

DELETE 1130   DELETE 1510   DELETE 1580   DELETE 1600   DELETE 1620

```
2000 DEF PROCcost
2010 FOR n = 1 TO N
2020 failures = failures + v(n,0)
2030 cost = ( failures * F + M ) / n
2040 PRINT "Maintain every ";STR$(n);" periods costs ;";cost
2050 NEXT n
2060 ENDPROC
```

DELETE 2070 et seq

Now check your listing against Program SCHEDC2 below.

Program 7.5 SCHEDC2: preventative maintenance class C2

```
  10 REM SCHEDC2
  20 REM MACHINE FAILURES AT PERIOD END ARE REPAIRED
  30 REM FINDS COST OF SCHEDULED MAINTENANCE CLASS C2
  35 REM EVERY n CALENDAR PERIODS
  40 DIM v(10,9),P(9,9)
  50 @%=&0002060A
  60
  70 PROCinput
  80 PROCstate_vector
  90 PROCcost
 100 END
 110
1000 DEF PROCinput
1010 INPUT "ENTER THE TOTAL NUMBER OF SYSTEM STATES ",I
1020 I = I-1
1030 v(0,0) = 1
1040 INPUT "ENTER THE COST OF REPAIR PER FAILURE ",F
1050 INPUT "ENTER THE COST OF MAINTENANCE ",M
1060 PRINT "ENTER THE MAXIMUM LENGTH OF THE MAINTENANCE"
1070 INPUT "CYCLE IN PERIODS ",N
1080 PRINT
1090 PRINT "ENTER THE ELEMENTS OF THE TRANSITION MATRIX"
1100 FOR i = 0 TO I
1110 FOR j = 0 TO I
1120 PRINT "P(";STR$(i);",";STR$(j);") = " ; : INPUT P(i,j)
1140 NEXT j
1150 NEXT i
1160 ENDPROC
1170
1500 DEF PROCstate_vector
1520 FOR n = 1 TO N
1530 FOR j = 0 TO I
1540 FOR i = 0 TO I
1550 v(n,j) = v(n,j) + v(n-1,i) * P(i,j)
1560 NEXT i
1570 NEXT j
1590 FOR j = 0 TO I
1610 NEXT j
1630 NEXT n
1640 ENDPROC
1650
2000 DEF PROCcost
2010 FOR n = 1 TO N
2020 failures = failures + v(n,0)
2030 cost = ( failures * F + M ) / n
2040 PRINT "Maintain every ";STR$(n);" periods costs ;";cost
2050 NEXT n
2060 ENDPROC
```

A RUN of SCHEDC2 with the data of Table 7.3 and 7.4 should confirm the results in Table 7.7.

Table 7.7   Cost of preventative maintenance policies class C2 from a RUN of SCHEDC2 with data of Tables 7.3 and 7.4

Maintain every n calendar periods	Expected cost
1	£ 95.00
2	£ 89.50
3	£ 97.93
4	£103.34
5	£104.90
6	£108.52
7	£108.84
8	£109.42
9	£110.20
10	£110.79

The optimum policy here is to maintain every two calendar periods at a cost which is slightly more expensive than that of the optimum policy of class C1 (see Table 7.6). However, the cost penalty for increasing the cycle length is less severe than before. The reader should now complete the Problems.

Problems

(7.1) Devise a PROCdata to read data into Program 7.2B LONGRUN from data statements as an alternative, which can exercised at the user's discretion, to conversational data input in PROCinput.

(7.2) Devise a PROCedit to allow the user to alter any part of the input to MARKOV.

(7.3) Develop LONGRUN to print out the value of E, the expected number of acceptable items produced by the machine in the example of Section 7.2.

(7.4) RUN LONGRUN for the transition matrix below and plot the n-stage transition probabilities $^{n}P_{1,0}$ $^{n}P_{1,1}$ $^{n}P_{1,2}$ for $n = 1, 2, \ldots, 8$ on the same graph.

$$P = \begin{matrix} .1 & .8 & .1 \\ .1 & .1 & .8 \\ .8 & .1 & .1 \end{matrix}$$

You should find that the probabilities $^{n}P_{1,j}$ exhibit damped oscillations which decay as n increases, leaving $p' = (1/3, 1/3, 1/3)$ in the steady state. P is an example of a 'doubly stochastic' matrix, since both rows and columns sum to unity, and the steady state probabilities are therefore equal.

(7.5) RUN Program LONGRUN for the following transition matrix P

$$P = \begin{array}{cccc} 0 & .5 & .5 & 0 \\ .5 & 0 & 0 & .5 \\ .5 & 0 & 0 & .5 \\ 0 & .5 & .5 & 0 \end{array}$$

You should find that the program prints a message 'SINGULAR P-I' and it cannot therefore find a steady state vector. You should also find that even powers of P are identical but different from odd powers of P. Can you account for this behaviour, and think of a necessary and sufficient condition for the existence of a steady state vector? (P is an example of a non-ergodic chain.)

(7.6) Rework the example of Section 7.2 under the new assumption that the repair of a failed machine takes two periods.

(7.7) A warehouse manager must decide whether or not to stock a 'slow moving' product. The weekly probability distribution of demand is .8, .1, .1 for 0,1,2 items respectively. What is the expected weekly long-run contribution to profits for the following cases if the storage cost is £5 per item per week, each sale contributes a gross profit of £25, demands which cannot be met ex-stock are lost and items which are ordered at the end of one week arrive at the beginning of the next?

(a) Order one item when stock on hand is zero.
(b) Order two items when stock on hand is zero.

Can you devise a better ordering rule?

(7.8) Suppose that the following data substitutes for that of Table 7.3

Cost of failure (disruption, etc.)	£300
Cost of repair	£ 50
Cost of maintenance	£ 25

Further suppose that a machine which has failed at the end of the nth period of continuous operation under a class C1 policy is not repaired *per se* at a cost of £50 but restored to working order at a cost of £25 as part of the scheduled maintenance. Modify SCHEDC1 to calculate the costs of this new policy.

(7.9) Use the data of Problem 7.8 to modify SCHEDC2 to calculate the costs of a modified class C2 policy of leaving the repair of a failed machine at the end of the nth period to scheduled maintenance.

*(7.10) The 'first-passage time' $T_{i,j}$ is the number of stages which are required to make a transition from state i to state j for the first time. $T_{i,j}$ is a random variable if j can be reached from i at all and it has a probability distribution $^n g_{i,j}$ which satisfies the recursive relationship

$$^n g_{i,j} = {}^n P_{i,j} - \sum_{t=1}^{n-1} {}^t g_{i,j} \, {}^{n-t} P_{j,j}$$

Develop MARKOV to print out $^n g_{i,j}$ for $n = 1,2,...,N$ for a given i and j.

*(7.11) The expected value of $T_{i,j}$ is denoted $t_{i,j}$ and satisfies

$$t_{i,i} = (p_i)^{-1}$$
$$t_{i,j} = 1 + \sum_{k<>j} P_{i,k} \, t_{k,j}$$

Develop LONGRUN to solve this set of simultaneous linear equations for a user input state j.

(7.12) Reformulate the model of Section 7.4 so that the original state s_0 is split into two distinct states s_{0f} and s_{0m} 'newly repaired' and 'newly maintained' respectively. Modify SCHEDC1 to work in this way, and in addition to print out the expected number of periods between overhaul given by $(p_{0,m})^{-1}$.

(7.13) Find the optimum level to restore stocks for the data of Problem 7.7 if in addition the items have a limited shelf life of two weeks and are fresh on delivery. Outdated stock is liquidated and the oldest stock items are sold first.

Hint: Be sure to enumerate all the system states.

(7.14) Redesign statements 1090 *et seq* in PROCinput for programs SCHEDC1 and SCHEDC2 to allow the user to input just the probability distribution for failure from the second column of Table 7.2. The array element $P(i,0)$ should be assigned the conditional probability of failure $^*p_i$ from a calculation as shown in the final column of Table 7.2 and $P(i,i+1)$ is assigned the value $1-P(i,0)$.

Index